We'll Have a Laugh

A Jovial Account of a
True Adventure from 1974

Andrew Nichols

Published by

MELROSE BOOKS

An Imprint of Melrose Press Limited
St Thomas Place, Ely
Cambridgeshire
CB7 4GG, UK
www.melrosebooks.co.uk

FIRST EDITION

Cover by Melrose Books

ISBN 978-1-909757-96-7

Printed and bound in Great Britain by:
Bell & Bain Limited, Glasgow

Contents

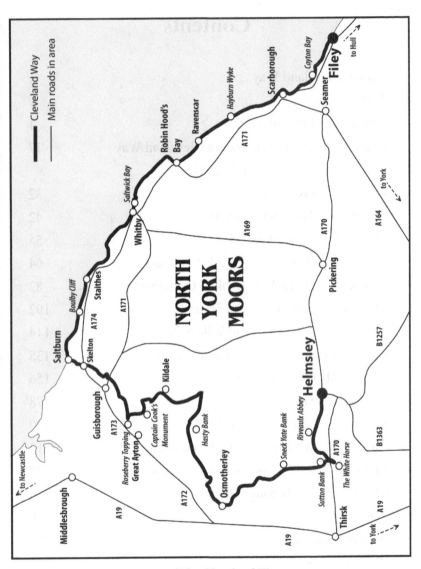

Map of The Cleveland Way

Author's Note

To really get a feel for the locations mentioned in this book I recommend you obtain a map of the North York Moors National Park. This will enable you to follow the intrepid explorers as they traverse the Cleveland Way. A basic map showing highlights is on the opposite page.

To get to know the era in which the book is set may I suggest listening to the music mentioned in the text. The year 1974 was at the height of the 'glam rock' period and many of the songs are indicative of that time. There are also more traditional tunes mentioned!

A playlist can be found at the back of the book.

The names used in this book have been mixed and spliced to avoid any embarrassment in real life. Hopefully, I haven't offended any of my friends and past acquaintances too much! Obviously, if I have caused offence then I apologise in advance!

I hope you enjoy reading this as much as I have enjoyed re-living it!

Chapter 1

Beginnings

Sixteen-year-old Andrew Price was bored. Bored with school, bored with collecting eggs at weekends on his dad's chicken farm, bored with not having a girlfriend, but above all else bored stiff with being bored. It didn't help having friends who 'did stuff'. All his mates seemed to be engaged in exciting weekend activities that eclipsed any of his own. The truth, of course, was very different, as in reality everybody in England in 1974 who was anywhere near sixteen years old thought the grass was far greener on the other side of the fence.

Mind you, school wasn't so bad. The beauty of being something of a swot meant most lessons at Melton Mowbray Upper School were, to Andrew at least, interesting. The teachers did their best to make the classes relevant and stimulating, but still something was missing. It would have helped if the biology teacher hadn't caught him playing 'footsie' with Sally Duckworth and then hadn't brought this, intended to be secret and erotic event, to the amused attention of everyone in the class. The sniggering laughter of his classmates was, of course, as effective at dampening the flames of passion as throwing a bucket of cold water over a couple of mating poodles on a street corner. Going any further with the gorgeous Sally was now highly unlikely! "I mean, surely that's the whole point of a biology practical, its reproductive biology in its raw human form," Andrew commented to his friends in the bus queue after school.

Youth club provided a diversion on Friday nights in the village. It meant a ten-minute ride on his moped, but that was part of the fun. Several of Andrew's mates had mopeds, all of them flasher and faster than the Raleigh Ultramatic he struggled along with, especially when the wind was blowing the wrong way! The moped owners at youth club were the elite. To enhance their stature they had all exchanged peaks from their helmets, so Andrew wore a white helmet with Martin's red peak, while Martin's red one sported Andrew's white peak. Sheer girl bait. Nothing could be sexier! To make the moped riders even more appealing to the opposite sex, various coloured stripes went from front to back in pairs on the helmets. These stripes were made from different coloured electrical tape. With such masculine embellishment, it was to the moped gang's amazement that women weren't throwing themselves under their bikes to be with them, and believe me they weren't! To further enhance their sex appeal riders would wear open shirts even in the coldest weather to show off their glorious chests, hairless not through waxing but sheer immaturity.

The Jenkins twins, Martin and Robert, had formed a band. Martin played lead guitar and his brother was on bass. Both were having guitar lessons and, frankly, the rock and folk music they bashed out was half decent. The singer was a tall, slim youth called Jeremy Ironcliffe. Jeremy was a great fan of Alvin Stardust. He wore the trademark single black glove and held the microphone in that unique Alvin Stardust way. Jeremy had a fine singing voice that well matched his Glam Rock, almost feminine, features. This look was enhanced by long blond hair, which flowed well over his shoulders. Watching Jeremy perform was brilliant. No singer in the history of singing did more gyrations and no singer in the history of serious song caused more laughter just through exaggerated movement.

The band was called Dutch Courage and featured butcher's delivery boy Derek Bowles on the drums. Derek possessed not only a drum kit, but a driver's licence as well. Even better, he was able to borrow his employer's delivery van after work to get the band to the various youth clubs where they performed. But a serious problem followed them to their performances. No matter how much they cleaned the interior of the van, the faint smell of pork sausages accompanied the group wherever they went. Unfortunately, this included when they were performing on stage.

The group managed to secure regular gigs throughout the Vale of Belvoir and quickly gained loyal fans from local teenage girls. They would arrive dressed to kill in skin-tight tops and bell-bottomed trousers, each trying to outdo the other in an attempt to 'get off' with one of the band members.

The boys certainly looked the part. They all wore pale blue turtleneck tops and Robert sported a large black floppy hat, in an attempt to look super cool, together with a red carnation hanging from the bottom of his guitar. Derek's bass drum had Dutch Courage, together with a large wine glass emblazoned across it, as was the style of the day. They played mainly rock music, songs such as 'Oh Boy!' and 'Rave On' by Buddy Holly were belted out by the band. 'Black Night' by Deep Purple gave the twins ample opportunity to show off their skills on guitar.

The Jenkins twins were also well known to those teachers who had the misfortune to attempt to educate them. Both were fairly short in stature with dark hair down to their shoulders. To those who knew them, telling them apart was easy. Martin, being second born by ten minutes, was slightly skinnier than his brother. Robert was stockier, more assertive and the dominant of the two. Despite being extremely cheeky and downright naughty at school, they were both likeable and generally pleasant young men.

The unique feature shared by the twins was one of fearlessness. This lack of fear manifested itself in many ways through their childhood but was particularly obvious when they were confronted by adult authority. The local fishponds in Long Clawson felt the full brunt of the twin's rebellious nature. Fees at the ponds were reasonable if you had some money. If you had none they were astronomical and for most of their youth the twins were in the latter category.

Fishermen were supposed to hold their catch in keepnets and then release it back into the pond when departing. The twins decided it was a good idea to 'stock' the pond in the next field. This pond had no fish and so would be available to them – for free – if fish 'miraculously' appeared in it. The chain of young men arriving to assist the one 'fee-paying twin' was nothing short of entrepreneurial. Fish were passed in plastic buckets from the successful fisherman along a willing column of helpers hiding in the hedgerow, to the peaceful confines of the farm pond. The problem was they got greedy. By the time the fishing member of the team packed up for the day the farm pond was wall-to-wall with carp. It would have been almost possible to walk across the pond on the backs of the fish without getting wet! Despite the local police being called and the event being mentioned in the local *Melton Times* newspaper, nobody was ever caught. So the twins got used to riding their luck.

For the twins, primary education was at the convent school in Melton Mowbray. For most students, the nuns were feared, but this was not the case with the twins. At the time a craze existed for hand held, paper fortune-telling devices known as Cootie Catchers or Chatterboxes, fashioned by the students. They were flicked into different configurations by the fingers of the student doing the fortune-telling. The student whose fortune was being told would select a number after each randomised flicking, which corresponded to a handwritten fortune or statement. Usually the result was something inappropriate such as 'fat face' or 'ugly mug', but at the time they were very popular with students. They were not so popular with the nuns. One of the teaching nuns demanded that all Chatterboxes were handed over at once. A friend of the twins, called Michael, stood up and sheepishly said he had one of these devices. Michael was the only person in the class, beside the twins, who shared a lack of respect for Roman Catholic education.

When asked to hand it over Michael simply held up his hand and mimed the movements associated with a Chatterbox. This brought a scream of anger from the nun, who proceeded to chase Michael around the classroom to the horror of the main body of students. The Jenkins twins, however, just sat and laughed. This resulted in the enraged nun bashing both twins on the head with a textbook every time she ran past them in pursuit of the daredevil with the imaginary Chatterbox!

At secondary school, the twins had been instigators of two notorious events that are well remembered by students of the era. The children of Long Clawson and Hose were taken to Belvoir High School in Bottesford by double-decker bus. Martin, Robert, Jeremy and most other young males rode upstairs unsupervised by driver and conductor. Just before Bottesford the road passes over the Grantham to Nottingham canal and sweeps around a bend in the road. Usually at this stage the driver was functioning on automatic pilot and was often going at quite a lick, probably in anticipation of a tea break coming up very soon.

Nobody remembers whose actual idea it was to try and tip the bus over, but the project was well received by all the lads on the upper floor. The primary organisers, though, were undoubtedly the Jenkins twins who, just before the corner was reached, directed everyone to one side of the bus. On the command 'go', given by Robert, all those on the top deck ran to the verge side of the bus, which immediately went up on two wheels. The bus then traversed the entire sweeping corner, some 50 yards, on just those two wheels! The whole time the terrified bus driver was attempting to save both the vehicle and his career.

As the bus slowed it bounced back over to the opposite two wheels, the changeover made more dramatic by all the youngsters on the top floor running at the right time to the other side. There was still, you understand, the suicidal desire to overturn the vehicle.

Finally, the bus ended up on four wheels and was immediately halted by the driver. At this point he promptly got out and proceeded to vomit, from pure shock and terror, on the roadside. The driver refused to continue and those students on the upper deck remained in detention every Friday afternoon for the rest of the term.

Not long afterwards, the Jenkins twins added to their reputation by taking their girlfriends under the school stage one lunch time for a kiss and a cuddle. The subterranean world beneath the stage was accessed via a trapdoor on top. Light was provided by a single candle. Unfortunately, the four young students lost track of time and were only made aware of that fact by the start of the drama class after lunch. The candle was nearly out and the girls were so scared that the twins had no choice but to knock on the base of the trapdoor to be 'rescued' by the teacher leading the drama class. Events such as this followed the Jenkins twins throughout their school careers, but they never lost their grins or their confidence.

Andrew Price was not involved with any such scurrilous

goings on. Apart from being something of a goody-goody, Andrew travelled to school on a different bus route, one which took in other small villages in the Vale of Belvoir including Stathern, Plungar, Barkestone-le-Vale and Redmile. In fact, Andrew Price only ever got put in detention once at secondary school, for talking in assembly. Detention was always on a Friday afternoon and was designed to take away the 'pleasure' of club afternoon, where students engaged in their chosen sporting activities.

Detention, on that fateful day, was taken by one of the more feared teachers, the deputy headmaster Mr Walbank. It was a beautiful summer afternoon when about a dozen ruffians (and Andrew Price) gathered in the detention room awaiting their fate.

Mr Walbank arrived and surprised them all by saying: "It's such a lovely day, let's go for a walk!"

The detention group spent the rest of the day looking at the remains of the Second World War airfield at Normanton, near Bottesford, and generally soaking up a very warm and pleasant afternoon. Walking past Bottesford church, Andrew, being a keen birdwatcher, spotted an unusual bird on the lower branches of a tree hanging over the River Devon.

"Excuse me, sir, but look at that, it's a pied flycatcher. It's the first one I've ever seen. Brilliant! Thanks for taking us on this walk sir, it's the best club afternoon I've ever had!"

The local youth club became the meeting point for many young people in the district. One local youth who became firm friends with Jeremy, the Jenkins twins and Andrew Price was an intense, honest and passionate young man called Joseph Krinn. Joseph – Joe to his friends – was a particular favourite of the youth club organisers as he had 'found God' big time! The first time Joe announced he had 'found God' he faced a number of questions as to where God had been hiding. Everyone else in the youth club seemed to find it difficult to accept that God was anywhere near Melton Mowbray and would certainly not reveal himself to a scruffy young man whose name had the anagram Penis J K Horn.

Joe was the least well off of the moped group and, like many others brought up in humble council house surroundings, was as generous as his hero Jesus Christ. Joe was the counsellor, the agony aunt and diplomat. Unfortunately, his intense religion did lead to a certain amount of ridicule. No one can forget the night Joseph chose to demonstrate 'speaking in tongues'. For weeks afterwards, his so-called 'friends' would pass him uttering gibberish but it didn't seem to worry him.

Typically, Joe would turn up at youth club wearing flared trousers, a coloured shirt, sleeveless cardigan and a parka with a white fur trim around the rim of the hood. When he was really dressing up, Joe would wear cream coloured flares and a grey shirt with a jet black velvet jacket. His shoulder length hair was often tousled and somewhat untidy. Joe had a fairly large 'Roman' nose and often walked with a staccato movement. In short, he walked like a woodpecker and he danced like a woodpecker on a red hot hotplate!

Joe's talents included song writing and poetry. He was also an avid collector of LPs and singles. If anyone wanted to know about popular musicians, song lyrics or discuss theology, Joe was the person to ask. He had a steady girlfriend, Yvonne, and, like Joe, she had a love of music and poetry. At school the two were inseparable and obviously very much in love. The only point of friction involved religion. Joe was deeply troubled by Yvonne's atheist comments, which were derived, in part, from the lyrics used by Emerson Lake and Palmer on their album *Tarkus*. Words that proclaimed that any god who didn't answer the screaming prayers of the millions killed in the Holocaust wasn't worth believing in. Conversely, Joe's theology was nurtured by his choice of music, the foremost being 'Question' by the Moody Blues with its line 'I'm looking for a miracle in my life', and including such lyrics as 'the road that I must choose'.

Yvonne saw the suffering in the world as evidence of atheism: that there was no God. Joseph figured that life itself, the love he felt all around him and the lack of suffering in their young lives proved the reverse. Both, however, felt that in some way they were 'undeserving'. Yvonne saw people as undeserving of suffering: Joseph saw himself as undeserving of God's love.

'Deep conversation' was one of Joe's trademarks. When he was in conversation with Robert Jenkins it often involved the mistreatment – by Robert – of Robert's girlfriends. Robert was notorious for the way he loved 'em and left 'em. He lived by the motto 'treat 'em mean and keep 'em keen'. This was much to the horror of Joe, who didn't see females as any sort of sex object at all. It's fair to say Joe was ahead of his time in thinking this way and, of course, it reflected his deeply held religious and moral views. Robert also had the reputation of taking other people's girlfriends, a dangerous practice that saw him in a fair amount of conflict with other young males. This again is where the fearless side of the Jenkins nature revealed itself, a side Joe found both morally reprehensible yet at the same time hilariously appealing.

With Martin or Jeremy, intense conversation usually involved females or song lyrics. With the latter, Joe saw much more than just a string of words thrown together to make a saleable chart topper. The music of the time, for him, held deep significance and meaning. Sometimes the latter met the former, making for some interesting conversations. For instance, when Yvonne introduced Joe to yet another Emerson, Lake and Palmer LP called *Brain Salad Surgery*, Joe feigned interest and pretended to like the music – the sole reason being that he adored the teenager dropping the stylus into the vinyl groove! Clutching at straws to make positive comment, Joe remarked on the great album cover. The whole effect was slightly sci-fi or alien-like and at the centre was the face of a beautiful woman. After dreamily listening to the album, Joseph was asked for comment. He hesitated then jumped in with: "Well, Yvonne, it's an interesting album!"

Then she asked the scary question: "Which is your favourite track?"

Hoping to appear confident and sophisticated, Joe replied: "Well, in all honesty, I liked the one with the wah-wah pedal. What's that one called again?"

"Trust you," she pointed out. "Trust you… it's called 'Still… You Turn Me On'!" Just for once Joseph was lost for words, as if someone had just shouted his deepest secret from the rooftops!

Philosophical conversations between Joe and Andrew were more fundamental. Andrew wasn't anywhere near as sophisticated in musical appreciation, poetry, politics or romance as Joe. Andrew was only really knowledgeable about the natural world, in particular in matters biological. Andrew was an unshakeable evolutionist and Joe a diehard creationist. If Andrew had been asked to contribute to any conversation on suffering he wouldn't have restricted his answer to the human race. In Andrew's eyes evolution didn't concern itself as to whether anything suffered or not, just as long as an individual reproduced itself before dying. The fact that Joe, Yvonne, or their immediate colleagues didn't appear to be 'suffering' was purely due to good luck! Maybe if they had been born 2,000 years earlier things would have been very different, and anyway, there were plenty of examples of people around them suffering. You only had to watch the television news to see that not everyone was leading the 'good life' in 1974. Despite heated discussions as to the meaning of 'life, the universe and everything', the two young men remained firm friends.

Joe's other passion was history. Not only did he excel at the subject academically, but he was keen on local history. He knew how old churches were, he knew where the battlefields were and the dates those conflicts occurred. Like many who are aware of the history of social progress, Joe was only too conscious of iniquities in the system. While not being a raging socialist, he recognised that around him were the 'haves' and 'have nots'. Joe was very vocal when the son of a local wealthy landowner obtained a 'full' grant for university by, as he saw it, 'cooking' the farm accounts in some way.

When the twins passed their driving tests an evening trip to the old deserted house above the village of Stathern was arranged. The house was named the 'murder house' and so it became a ghost hunting trip. Joe refused to be part of it and waited at the end of the track while the twins, Jeremy and Andrew drove in.

"Let's have a laugh," Robert announced. "Let's put Martin and Jeremy in the boot and race back to Joe and tell him they went crazy and ran off with a ghost!"

An Oscar-winning performance from Robert and Andrew saw Joe totally convinced that something deeply satanic was occurring. He threw himself on his knees and began to pray for his wandering friends. All in all, he took it surprisingly well when the boot opened and Martin and Jeremy emerged with hoots of laughter and grins!

Jeremy Ironcliffe lived in the same village as the twins. Jeremy's parents knew the Jenkins and so, even though they attended different junior schools, they became friends from an early age. Only at secondary school (Belvoir High School in Bottesford) did they find themselves sharing classrooms. Like Joe, Jeremy had a love of music, which of course is why he was well placed to be appointed lead singer in the band.

Jeremy, being a tall, slim individual with long hair and fairly delicate features, was without doubt one of the most naturally good-looking young men in the district. Nicknamed Jez, he was a well-liked, but often quiet and aloof, individual. If anything, Jeremy was prone to complain when the going got tougher than usual. He was extremely keen on football and, even from a young age, played for Long Clawson in the local village league. For many years, Jeremy was centre forward as he had a killer instinct when it came to scoring goals.

One of Jeremy's idiosyncrasies was a strong desire to always get the last laugh. It is true to say that Jeremy would do or say anything to get a laugh, especially at school. In English literature class, Joe and Jeremy were the only males in a class of twelve pupils. During *Tess of the d'Urbervilles*, Jeremy picked up on the transformation that occurred when Tess went from virtuous maiden to unmarried mother with child — a transformation that was rich in literary metaphor, but deficient in sordid detail. In fact, very deficient in the type of sordid detail the two male students had been patiently waiting for! Jeremy raised his hand and, in serious tones, enquired if the book was missing a few pages between Tess 'falling on the grass' and Tess 'carrying a bundle'!

Like the twins, Jeremy had one unusually outstanding comedic claim to fame during his school career. The head-master at Melton Upper School, this being the school students progressed to after secondary school in Bottesford, was a much feared individual who always wore a professorial gown and mortar board for assembly. To the pupils he was 'master over' he appeared to lack a sense of humour. Maybe he perceived this lack of connection with his flock, or maybe some well-meaning member of the teaching staff tipped him off. Whatever the reason, at one assembly he decided to act 'younger' and conciliatory. Still draped in his scary gown, he offered the olive branch of reconnection to the gathered students. Desperately, he reached out to the stunned pupils in a speech studded, inappropriately, with the grammar of the day and ending with a flurry of his 'Batman' robes and the incongruous statement that whatever happens, if anyone needed his help or advice, 'I'll be there'! As if any of the assembled multitude would have approached this terrifying teacher with anything short of a life-threatening injury inflicted by, for example, a javelin.

At this point, Jeremy began to sing, somewhere near the back of the hall, words by the Jackson Five. Words from the song 'I'll Be There', which were well known to all the students in the auditorium and, incredibly, were taken up by everyone, leaving the headmaster utterly and completely flummoxed. On the one hand, he could hardly discipline an entire hall for being disrespectful, especially not when attempting to be 'hip' and pleasant. But on the other hand, the look on his face spelt out confusion and a complete failure to understand the 'moment'. As he completed the statement 'I'll be there', Jeremy kicked in tunefully with:

"You and I must (joined now by the congregation!)
    make a pact,
We must bring salvation back,
Where there is love, I'll be there!"

And they continued in superb harmony to the astonished stares of the entire teaching staff with:

"I'll reach out my hand to you,
I'll have faith in all you do,
Just call my name and I'll be there!"

Brilliant! And nobody has ever forgotten that Jeremy was the instigator: except the teachers, of course, who had no idea at all where that bit of mass disobedience had emerged from.

Apart from lusting after Sally Duckworth and messing about at the youth club, Andrew loved the outdoors. As a child, Grandad Price had taken the time to point out all the farmland birds. Things such as yellowhammers singing 'little bit of bread and no cheese please' and wood pigeons cooing 'me toe bleeds daddy', were very much part of life. With a pair of binoculars permanently 'borrowed' from his father and a tattered copy of *The Observer's Book of Birds*, Andrew would often wander the escarpment above the Vale of Belvoir (the 'Vale'), slowly turning into a knowledgeable ornithologist. This intense love of nature made studying A-level geography, botany and zoology an easy and natural choice at Melton Mowbray Upper School.

Despite birdwatching, school and weekend farm work, boredom still reigned supreme for Andrew Price. Something needed to be done.

Andrew's father could see his son was bored and decided some parental guidance was required. Mike Price was a Yorkshireman with a deep and abiding love of the county. As a child he had spent the war years on a farm just outside the village of Sessay, below the North York Moors National Park. The farm was in sight of that great landmark the White Horse of Kilburn. Mike had recently read a newspaper article on a newly-opened long distance footpath called the Cleveland Way.

The Cleveland Way is one of Britain's oldest long distance walks and was officially opened just four years after the Pennine Way, in May 1969, at Helmsley Castle. The 100-mile hike begins in Helmsley and skirts the western edge of the North York Moors National Park. When the walk reaches the coastal town of Saltburn-by-the-Sea, at its northern extremity, the path turns south-east and then goes down the coastal section of the National Park, finishing up at Filey.

Basically, the walk almost encircles the National Park. The moors themselves are an easily defined geographical area with distinctive heather moors, wooded valleys and farmland, which is often framed by dry stone walls.

The physical boundaries of the National Park are sharply visible. Firstly, there is a gentle, rolling farmland transition, marking the southern boundary against the Vale of Pickering and Vale of York. Secondly, there is a steep moorland escarpment running alongside the northern section of the Vale of York, the Vale of Mowbray and the district of Cleveland. Finally, there is the eastern boundary, in reality running north-east to south-east, making the moors roughly triangular. This edge is characterised by rugged coastal cliffs bordering farmland. The cliffs drop away to rocky or sandy beaches with the North Sea beyond. The well-known seaside towns of Scarborough and Whitby fall within this section of the North York Moors and create an interesting contrast to the wild and rugged areas of the National Park.

The walk looked like something Mike would love to have done himself, but chicken farming, debt, marriage and family didn't leave time for such indulgence. That's why Christmas 1973 saw Andrew receive a small Dalesman publication, written by Bill Cowley, entitled simply *The Cleveland Way*.

This was accompanied by a map, bearing the same name, depicting the entire route of this wonderful new hiking track around the North York Moors. Boxing Day became a day of glorious study for Andrew and by nightfall a brand new way of relieving boredom had entered his thoughts.

Walking the Cleveland Way in its entirety during the next school holiday was suddenly a priority. Convincing his friends to accompany him was the next challenge!

Chapter 2

The Leicestershire Cleveland Way Appreciation Society

Six months before being gifted the 'Cleveland Way introduction pack', way back in June 1973, Andrew Price turned sixteen. The open road now beckoned and his moped era began. Mike Price had purchased the second-hand, fire-red Raleigh moped several weeks before Andrew's birthday. Upon grateful receipt of the bike, Andrew was off up Harby Hills and out on to the Scalford road heading for Melton. Unfortunately, nobody had filled the fuel tank and so the first trip out saw Andrew knocking at a farmer's door asking to use the phone to effect a rescue. This was made all the more embarrassing when, on retrieval of the bike, his dad pointed out the small fuel cock lever, which on being pushed through 90 degrees opened a reserve fuel tank built into the main reservoir.

All the other members of the youth club's moped gang were somewhat more experienced than Andrew, having already had a year under their belts as they were all a year older. Robert Jenkins was the proud owner of a Garelli, while his brother Martin had an NSU Quickly. Joseph Krinn rode a Puch Maxi and Jeremy buzzed round on a Honda PC50.

The summer of 1973 saw a 'steam fest' over towards Six-Hills, which the moped owners decided to attend. A beautiful, sunny, June day had its peace and quiet shattered by five mopeds, throttles held wide open to milk every last bit of speed from the small 49cc engines, screaming along past Ab Kettleby on the top road. Joseph seemed to be particularly enjoying God's creations, so much so he failed to observe the special constable with his hand in the stop position at the gateway to the steam fest. He only noticed the stop hand when a car, being directed into the parking field by the busy constable, came screaming to a halt.

Joe pulled up and the policeman walked over to him. Maybe this particular officer was having a bad day, maybe he had climbed out of his bed on completely the wrong side. Whatever it was, he proceeded to deliver an incredible telling off to the one person in the moped gang who least deserved it. All credit to Christianity, though, as Joe simply apologised before joining the rest of the group smiling as if nothing had happened.

All things considered, the moped gang were not that bad. Only when going places in the Jenkins's spare car, which the twins were allowed to drive, did things ever deteriorate. The best trick was to park in a lay-by late at night and gather outside around the front of the vehicle. When the car became illuminated by the headlights of a passing vehicle, everyone would bounce it up and down, making it look like Casanova himself was engaged in some nefarious physical activity within! This activity stopped abruptly one night when the twins' parents spotted their spare car rocking outrageously and reversed back up to see what was going on. An embarrassed group of young men tried to explain the problems they all thought the suspension was enduring, hence the 'shake test' of the car!

The youth club encouraged all sorts of activities and a camping trip to Derbyshire saw Andrew, Joe, Jeremy and the twins under canvas in the Peak District. Admittedly, this camp had the added distraction of females who proved willing participants in alarming passing motorists. No bouncy vehicles this time, just Andrew in the dark with an anorak pulled over his head who stood, statue-like, on a trig point next to the road. The other happy campers illuminated him by torch light, giving the illusion of a visitation from the 'ghost of a headless hunter'. How this didn't cause an accident was a miracle and was probably due to more anguished prayers from Joseph.

The introduction to camping, which youth club trips provided, was to prove invaluable once the decision to walk the Cleveland Way was finally taken. Lessons learned included setting up camp, packing rucksacks correctly and choosing easy foods to prepare and carry. Basic knowledge, necessary to enable an expedition to be planned, was gained during those early youth club trips to Derbyshire and Wales. Other skills, such as sneaking into the girls' tents for a hurried kiss and a tentative grope, were incidental perks of the learning process!

One of the youth club organisers, Terry, was not only there to impart religious and moral instruction, but made it his business to pass on map reading skills that were to prove invaluable. Those showing any interest were encouraged to understand and appreciate the full glory that OS maps contained: how contour lines could be interpreted to show how undulating a track was likely to be, how to hold the map with the grid lines going north-south and how to use a compass to check direction, enabling safe walking across open country on a bearing. Interpreting maps became a joy to most of the young people who were fortunate enough to be guided by Terry at youth club. Robert and Andrew became particularly adept at using maps to get from A to B and in understanding the variety of obstacles they might encounter on the way.

One other very useful thing to come from youth club was a

short first aid course held at the home of a middle-aged nurse from Old Dalby. Everyone tried to learn about compression bandages and artificial resuscitation, but it was difficult to concentrate. Difficult due to the fact that the middle-aged and attractive nurse insisted on wearing a top that revealed a beautiful, firm pair of breasts every time she leaned over. Trying to find excuses to get this well-endowed woman to lean forward, far enough for a good hard stare, became a game all the young males participated in, except, of course, Joe. Maybe this is why he was selected to do the compression part of resuscitation using the busty nurse as the model. On the way home afterwards, Joe expressed complete ignorance of any lustful thoughts while he was pushing down on the woman's chest. Actually, Joe was shocked and horrified that the rest of the group was profoundly envious of him getting so close to the lovely nurse. He went to great lengths to remind everyone that the nurse was at least 40 years old. He was equally horrified when Robert made the observation that age had nothing to do with it; the lady simply had a beautiful pair of breasts! Looking back, it's hard to imagine that both the nurse and her husband weren't well aware of what the first aid students were up to! Maybe they were as titillated as their students by the proceedings!!

Christmas 1973 came and went. The Cleveland Way guidebook was read and re-read by Andrew Price. The cold and wet months of January and February passed by. All the time, Andrew was thinking of the Cleveland Way. Finally he decided that the time was ripe. Flushed with knowledge of this Yorkshire hiking path, an excited Andrew approached his moped mates.

"There's something I want to talk to you about. Can you come to my place Saturday night about 6 o'clock? Chris Hewson and Andreas Christakos have already said they'll be there. I've got an idea for something we can all do at Easter."

"What is it?" Jeremy asked.

"I'm not telling you today, you'll have to come to my place on Saturday to find out properly," said a secretive Andrew. Reluctantly, all agreed to be there. Nobody objected to the presence of Chris or Andreas, even though they were a year younger than the moped mob and not members of the youth club. They were Andrew's friends from school and at that stage were only vague acquaintances of the rest of the gang.

Andreas was better known as 'Dreas, or now and again as Zorba the Greek. He was an olive-skinned individual whose father was indeed Greek. Alex Christakos had a very excitable nature. He ran a small pig fattening unit as well as teaching biology at a Nottingham high school. Andreas shared his father's excitable nature and Greek good looks. Girls fancied Andreas, until they got close enough to make out an incredibly spotty face with numerous 'active volcanoes'. These 'volcanic hot spots' bore all the signs of recent and on-going 'eruptions'. Despite this temporary disability, Andreas shared a happy-go-lucky philosophy on life, very like Joe, but without intense religion.

Andreas was very taken with comedy programmes on television and was the one most likely to use catchphrases from them. In 1974, most families would watch television together in the evenings and discussion of the previous night's broadcast was the main topic of break time conversation at school. Andreas derived great popularity owing to his ability to imitate characters from *Dad's Army*, *Some Mothers Do 'Ave 'Em* and *Are You Being Served?* Unfortunately, his quotations fell on deaf ears when he was with Andrew Price as Andrew's parents exerted considerable restraint as far as viewing hours were concerned. They imposed a regime of strict censorship on productions they deemed to be unsuitable!

Andrew had been friends with Andreas since Belvoir High School days and would often sit next to him on the bus. Once they had both turned fifteen, Mr Christakos would take Andreas and Andrew to after-school discos at his school in Nottingham. City students were, and probably still are, far more fashion conscious than their rural counterparts. A group of Nottingham 'sophisticates' dressed in cheese cloth shirts with penny round collars, brogues and tank tops approached the country bumpkins at one of these functions.

"What are flares? Do you know?" the leader of an aggressive pack of city youths enquired.

Andreas replied: "They're things that shoot into the sky and burst alight to say there's a ship in trouble." It was some weeks later before both Andreas and Andrew realised flares were the latest trouser design and that's why that particular group of Nottingham youths had laughed so loudly at Andreas's answer.

To say that Andreas and Andrew were inept when it came to relationships with females was an understatement. Andrew was frankly scared stiff of the female of the species, despite being acutely aware that to be biologically successful he had to get very, very, close to one, or more, eventually! Andreas, on the other hand, was supremely confident in his ability to attract the opposite sex. In his opinion it wasn't his fault he hadn't had any joy in that direction as yet.

Unfortunately, Andreas was prone to say incomprehensible and ambiguous comments at the early stages of flirtation with young ladies. As the girls were equally inexperienced, these comments came across as challenging or just plain weird. A prime example was at the last school disco they attended courtesy of Mr Christakos. Two girls were dancing without boyfriends on the dance floor. Andrew agreed to accompany

Andreas on a rare excursion to try their luck. Prior to making their bold entrance, Andrew accepted he would be trying for the plumper of the two, a girl who danced rather unusually by flailing her arms from side to side. Even before entering 'the fray', on the dance floor, Andreas had rather ungraciously nick-named her 'Orang-utan'. Andreas, of course, picked the more physically attractive member of the pair, a girl so obviously out of his league that he shouldn't even have glanced in her direction, let alone assumed she would consider dancing with him. Still, the lights were subdued so she would be unlikely to notice the imminent eruption of 'Krakatoa' on the 'Pacific Rim' of plebs currently gaining in size on his cheek!

In all fairness, the girls did allow the two country bumpkins to dance with them. But when the song stopped conversation was expected! Thankfully, one of the teachers announced the imminent raffle ticket draw, after which an awkward silence descended. For too long, Andrew and Andreas stood silent. For too long, the girls anxiously waited for the opening line. Andreas took control and delivered a first line that was so misunderstood by the girls they simply walked off shaking their heads in disgust. Andreas leaned forward and bellowed in the pretty girl's ear:

"Is this your lucky night?"

Unfortunately, when he leaned over, she became close enough to detect 'lava flow' on Andreas's face and, failing to realise he meant 'lucky with the raffle ticket', decided it definitely wasn't his lucky night and took off like a ferret down a rabbit hole.

Somewhat despondently, the two would-be suitors walked off to the tune of '(I Can't Get No) Satisfaction' by the Rolling Stones; a very appropriate refrain — the whole experience leaving them both emotionally scarred for life.

Chris Hewson was well known to everyone in the group as his father taught history at Melton Upper School. Also, Chris was a natural sportsman and played tennis, badminton and football for the school. He also followed the professional football games and, like Jeremy, was very knowledgeable on the position of teams in the top four league tables. He was an avid supporter of Liverpool football club and firmly upheld the view that the 1973/74 season would see the team win the FA Cup.

Chris also sailed competitively in the family's Mirror sailing dinghy in flooded gravel pits near Melton. Chris was tall with curly, fair hair and was conspicuously last to start shaving. Not that those who were shaving at this stage were really tackling much in the way of testosterone-induced foliage. Chris, however, was noticeably only sprouting delicate 'bum fluff', as people would have called it. Interestingly, nobody would ever have said that to Chris's face because it just wouldn't have been appropriate. All the more fascinating as Chris was want to say the most tactless, hurtful and inappropriate things to his friends and think it hilarious! Quite frankly, Chris was sarcastic and quite cruel in the way he would mercilessly ridicule his friend's idiosyncrasies in front of others. Somehow, though, he got away with it and was generally a very popular individual.

A prime example of Chris Hewson being tactless concerned his dealings with Martin Jenkins. Chris knew the twins as they too sailed occasionally in the same gravel pits. Martin, while not having a girlfriend in the early months of 1974, had certainly known love. His *inamorato* in late 1973 was a delightful and scholastic girl of the same age called Janet. After about three months of going out together, Martin managed to persuade Janet to indulge in a naked romp in his parents' double bed while they were away from home on a short holiday. The full love making thing failed to occur, but even so, Janet made Martin swear to keep their bedroom foray a secret, on the threat of terminating the relationship if he didn't. Naturally, the first thing Martin did was show off his 'almost' conquest by filling Andrew in on the sordid details and making him swear not to tell a soul! Naturally, the first thing Andrew did was tell Chris! Unfortunately, Andrew relied on Chris not being tactless enough to mention this titillating tale to anyone else, certainly not Martin himself. Andrew just took it as read that this level of secrecy would be upheld. This trust in Chris proved disastrous for all concerned.

About a week later, Andrew, Martin and Janet were seated at a table attending a hoedown held in one of the dance halls in Melton Mowbray. Hoedowns and discos were the main social venue for many young people at the time. Hoedowns featured lots of quaint antics such as country style 'promenades', which were only surpassed by the caller's command to 'swing your partner round'; at times positively dangerous, but so unforgettably exhilarating.

Chris Hewson walked into the venue, strode purposefully up to their table, looked at Martin and Janet and said, in a loud voice: "I hear you two have been a bit naughty then! Whe-e-e y!"

Andrew and Martin looked at Chris with absolute horror. Janet wasted no time at all and simply got up and walked away, Martin followed in an attempt to salvage his relationship, leaving Andrew Price staring at Chris.

"What the hell did you say that for? You're unbelievable, Chris! Surely you realised that was a confidence?"

It was some weeks before Martin was civil to either Andrew or Chris. Needless to say, everyone learned from the experience, but thanks to it, Martin lost the love of his life.

Interestingly, the last person Martin himself would have told was Chris, as Martin was wise enough to know better.

Chris, Andreas and Andrew were in the same year at school and did biology and geography together. Somehow, though, Andreas and Chris had resisted the moped craze, or more likely their parents had resisted it for them.

Saturday night came around and saw a curious group of young men sat round the living room table at the home of the Price family. A mixed plate of plain and chocolate digestive biscuits was on the table in front of them, as was a large map featuring the North York Moors and the Cleveland Way. The chocolate biscuits were disappearing fast, but only later did it emerge that Joe was turning them over so it looked as if only plain digestives were left. This was revealed when long after the chocolate biscuits had apparently run out, Joe was somehow still eating them. If Joseph had been feeding the 5,000 he would have been eating full-sized cod while everyone else was on sardines!

"I want us all to walk the Cleveland Way this Easter, that's why I've got you all here. I want to do it and I reckon it would be a brilliant adventure for all of us," announced Andrew as an opening gambit.

"Where's the Cleveland Way," asked Robert.

"How long is it? And how many years will we be gone?" Martin unenthusiastically enquired.

"We'll have to camp 'cos I can't afford hotels or anything," said Joe, shoving yet another chocolate biscuit down his gullet.

"Give me a chance to explain," said Andrew. "It's just over 100 miles long."

A collective groan and a few well-chosen swear words were bandied around. "One hundred flippin' miles!" exclaimed Jeremy. "Can't we do it on mopeds?"

"No we can't do it on blooming mopeds. Listen and ask questions later. It's 100 miles long and it starts in Helmsley in Yorkshire. Here look at the map!" Andrew pointed to the map and put his finger on the start point. "It starts here and goes over here to Sutton Bank. Then we go down to the White Horse for a look…"

Andreas interrupted. "What's the White Horse? I mean do you think some flippin' animal is still going to be there when we do this walk?"

"Don't be so daft, 'Dreas, it's on the hillside and made from limestone spread over the rocks. It's about 300 feet long and it was made in the 1850s by a local school teacher and his pupils – we have got to see it up close!" Andrew carried on. "After that, we back track to Sutton Bank and then continue right around the edge of the moors, right up here to Saltburn-by-the-Sea. Then we come down the coast, all the way past Whitby and Scarborough to Filey." Andrew's finger traced the route making the walk seem deceptively swift and smooth. In the background, Andreas was heard muttering, "Hi-ho, Silver."

"Can't we just walk straight across from Helmsley to Filey, instead of going around in a great big circle?" asked an incredulous Jeremy.

"No, of course not," a slightly annoyed Andrew retorted. "This book tells you all about it." Andrew said, holding up the book he had been gifted at Christmas. "You can all take it in turns to borrow it and read up on the Cleveland Way, if you want to. The walk goes the long way round from Helmsley to Filey. The scenery sounds fantastic: there's moorland, wood-land, hills, dales, rivers, seaside, cliffs, birds and farming."

"What about historical things like ruins or battlefields?" Joe asked as he began to understand the possibilities such an adventure presented.

"Read the guidebook, Joe! There are all sorts of historical things like old abbeys and castles. This walk's got the lot, we've got to do it! If we don't do it now we never will. It's something we'll all remember for the rest of our lives – please say you'll do it! We'll have to carry camping gear and enough food and clothes to last about ten days. Dad says he'll take us in his Transit van and he'll pick us up at the end in Filey." An excited Andrew Price could see he was beginning to win his friends over.

"If we get that far!" said Jeremy, who seemed to be the only one offering any negatives. Everyone else was silent and deep in thought.

"You're going to bore us all shitless with birds if we go on this walk aren't you, Andrew?" commented Andreas.

"I thought I'd try, 'Dreas, but then you need educating, don't you! 'What are flares? Oh they're things that shoot in the sky to warn ships!' Yep, you need educating all right!" chided Andrew, which effectively shut Andreas up.

"When exactly are we going to go? That's if we say yes, of course!" Martin asked.

"Well, the first Monday of the Easter holidays is April 8th. Dad reckons he can take us up to Helmsley in his van nice and early on that day. That gives us all day to get across to Sutton Bank and maybe further before we camp. It means we will be walking right through Easter and finish sometime during the middle of the next week. As I say, the most it should take us is ten days," Andrew replied.

"Where will we camp?" Chris asked.

"I'm not entirely sure, but there is a campsite at Osmotherley and several suitable spots along the coast, like Robin Hood's Bay and Scarborough." Andrew added: "I've read the guide-book and reckon the first night we will have to find a farm paddock or something, but then we can aim on being at the Osmotherley site by the second night. After that, we can just do our best to cover at least ten or twelve miles a day. Down the coast, we should find proper campsites, but we can't book anything 'cos we just don't know how fast or slow we're going to be, especially as we'll be carrying full camping kit!" Andrew added, pointing at the places mentioned on the map.

"We'll need wet-weather gear and decent rucksacks," Chris added thoughtfully.

"We'll have to share tents." Martin said. "I'm not sleeping in the same tent as me brother. He stinks."

"So do you, Mart," Robert quickly added.

This resulted in the first of many fights the twins were to have over the coming weeks. Not that they weren't expected, as rivalry between first-born Robert and second-born Martin had always been intense. It wasn't unusual for friends of the twins to find themselves dodging flailing fists as they attempted to separate the pair and stop them causing actual bodily harm to one another. Strangely though, the twins themselves never seemed to sustain any real injury during these fights, invariably the rescuers were the ones who came off worst.

"The Easter holidays are five weeks away. That gives us plenty of time to plan this out and decide which tents to take and what gear we need. I just want to know by the end of next week who's in and who's out. In a couple of weeks, we'll meet again and start making proper plans," Andrew postulated.

"Can I just say something in support of this walk, please?" asked Joseph, with a philosophical look on his face.

"Not if you're going to start quoting Elton John, or reckon Marc Bolan predicted in one of his convoluted lyrics that you were destined to walk the Cleveland Way," said a cynical Andrew.

"No, what I want to say is this – we are all at a cross roads. In particular Robert, Jez, Martin and I because in a few months we leave school. Who knows where we will be this time next year! I want to go to university, Rob's going to study food technology, Martin reckons he'll be working somewhere and Jez, well what will he be doing? Hairdressing or something?"

"Thanks, Joe. Thanks a lot mate!" replied a very annoyed Jeremy.

"Sorry, Jez! But you all know what I mean. We are going on a big journey when we finish school and we might lose touch with each other. Listen to Jim Croce's song 'Time in a Bottle', released just before he was killed in that plane crash last year. Killed in a plane crash! I mean, some of us might be dead and gone soon, you just don't know how long you've got! Frankly, we don't have much time for anything and every second is precious."

"You're dead right, Andy!" Martin said, still digesting a comment Andrew had made earlier. "How do you do it, Joe? You always seem to find song lyrics foretelling our fate, or explaining why we all did something after the event!" Martin had a look of genuine respect for Joe's musical knowledge.

Joseph continued: "I reckon we need to go on this walk because it's part of a much bigger journey we're embarking on – life – and, who knows, this might be our last true taste of freedom, certainly with us all together, anyway. It might not be long before some of us are married for crying out loud!"

Joseph's words seemed to ring true and a profound silence engulfed the meeting.

"So, are you all going to let me know by the end of next week if you're game to do it or not?" asked Andrew, for a second time.

A collective and surprisingly enthusiastic 'all right' ended the first meeting of the unofficial Leicestershire Cleveland Way Appreciation Society.

Much to the relief of Andrew Price over the next few days, everyone present – even the seemingly reluctant Jeremy – indicated that they were game to walk the Cleveland Way over the Easter holidays.

The expedition was on!!

Chapter 3

Preparation

Two weeks later, the entire group met again, this time at the home of the twins. Since the previous meeting, Andrew had been taken on a 'clothes shop' by his mother and was sporting a brown jacket that, according to his mother, looked 'smart'. It was easier at the time of purchase to go along with his mother's ideas of what looked smart, but now, among his peers, the selection of this brown corduroy jacket was looking like a very bad idea.

"Please tell us you're not wearing that on the Cleveland Way," implored Martin.

"Please tell us you'll never wear it again," added his brother Robert, looking around the assembled group for approval. This was a new way of teasing the ever gullible and easy to poke fun at Andrew.

Such taunts were the bane of Andrew's life. In short, the studious and parent-dominated Andrew was an easy target. His hobby of birdwatching was, in 1974 at least, a nerdy sort of activity usually conducted by elderly people wearing tweed or corduroy jackets.

"At least you look like a birdwatcher with that brown jacket," added Martin, feeling somewhat empowered by the looks of approval his teasing was gaining from the others in the room.

"Actually, you look like a great tit wearing it," added

Jeremy, keen to throw his weight behind the ridicule.

The main problem Andrew had faced throughout his life was well-meaning, but domineering, parents. Up to a couple of years ago, his Yorkshire father had applied daily doses of thick cream to his hair in order to create a 'quiff' that was stylish among much older men. It was a quiff proudly sported by Mike Price with his thick head of hair, with or without a liberal dose of hair cream. In Andrew's case, even if cement had been used it was doubtful that his unruly hair would have retained any shape at all, let alone a sixties-style quiff! Unfortunately, parental application of hair cream, long after it was fashionable to have it, simply provided even more fodder for his peers to use in ridicule. When attending Melton swimming baths with the school it wasn't uncommon to hear taunts of "don't swim behind Price whatever you do, there's a bloody oil slick!" The taunts had come from Chris Hewson and were quite typical of the way he treated his friends!

The meeting finally settled down and Andrew was able to establish some control, albeit with the brown jacket hanging in the hall on a coat stand. Interestingly enough, his mum always wondered why the jacket was never worn again!

"Right, we've got to get organised so next time we meet up we can bring all the stuff we're going to take," was Andrew's opening line.

"I've got a tent that sleeps two," said Jeremy, "but whoever shares with me has to help carry it!"

Chris Hewson, being the all-round sportsman, knew a thing or two about tents and was quick to add some salient points on living under canvas.

"Has it got a ground sheet sewn in and a separate fly sheet? We've got to have good gear. We've got to be safe."

The last few words indicated that it wasn't Chris speaking,

but his dad, who was obsessed with safety in everything he did. Mr Hewson was quite unlike all the other teachers – in short he was well ahead of his time. Chris's school teacher father was not, however, the most humorous of chaps, but he was trained in first aid and was often first to be sent for when a child was injured at school. One of the few times Mr Hewson was seen to smile was when he was called to the woodwork room after the teacher in charge fainted, much to the consternation of the pupils in his class. Had Chris not overheard his parents talking no one would have known the cause of the smile on Mr Hewson's face, visible to all, when he returned from his first aid administrations to resume teaching his history class.

"You'll never believe why old Smithy fainted in woodwork," said Chris to Andrew and Andreas after lunch the next day. "He was that annoyed with Curly Turner for breaking a chisel on the lathe that he ran over to belt him, like he does, and he caught his balls on one of the benches. Dad was wetting himself when he told Mum last night!"

"Chris is right; we do have to be safe. All the tents should be as light as possible, have separate fly sheets and sewn-in groundsheets," added Andrew.

"We can get the two-man tent from youth club," said Joe.

"I'm sleeping with you then," said Martin.

"When you say you're sleeping with him, does that mean you're zipping your sleeping bags together Mart?" added his brother Robert, who was still in 'piss-take' mode following his successful session earlier with Andrew.

"Sod off, Robert!" shouted Martin, who immediately launched an all-out attack on his brother. This led to the others having to pull the protagonists apart and resulted in Jeremy intercepting a punch from Robert that caused quite a nasty cut to his lip. Joe, of course, being a peace-loving Christian, avoided the violence. This, incidentally, allowed him time to eat two extra chocolate biscuits he had surreptitiously upturned earlier in order to make them look like plain digestives.

"Are you two finished? I mean look what you've done to him," an outraged Andreas was pointing at Jeremy, who had blood running down his chin.

"Don't worry about me – look at him!" Jeremy was speaking through blood-stained teeth while pointing at Joe. "How the hell does that bastard always end up eating chocolate biscuits. I mean we finished them ages ago!"

"He's right Joe, he's bloody right!" Andreas exclaimed.

Joe just smiled and happily continued chewing.

"Yeah, with the emphasis on the word bloody, he's definitely bloody right," Andrew added, pointing out the mess Jeremy was now making as drops of blood fell on the Jenkins' brand new shag pile carpet.

"Get something, Robert, you red-nose, I mean you hit him," implored Martin. Robert shrugged and left the room, returning with Andrew's brown jacket.

"No way, Rob," said Andrew snatching it back. Andreas saved the day by racing to the downstairs loo and returning with an armful of toilet paper.

Through all this, Chris had been laughing. Only as things calmed down did the rest of the group begin to notice this interesting phenomenon. Nobody said anything, but it did seem very odd that, in the midst of crisis (one that involved aggression and bloodshed), a member of the expedition's team was displaying what could only be termed as an 'inappropriate emotional response'!

Joseph had been deep in thought after hearing Martin admonish his twin brother. "Martin, what do you mean calling Robert a red-nose? I mean it's Jeremy who's actually bleeding!"

Martin smiled at the group. "You mean you don't know the red-nose joke!"

Everyone shook their heads in the 'no' direction. "Well, I'll tell it then! There's this chap who goes to the circus, a little chap with a bald head. He's sitting there watching the clowns when the lights go dim and a spotlight shines right on him. The clown points at him and shouts: 'Hey you!'

To which the little guy says: 'Who, me?'

'Yeah, you!' says the clown. 'Tell me, are you a left arse?'

'No,' says the little guy.

'Are you a centre arse?'

'No.'

'Then you must be a right arse! Ha ha ha ha!' said the aggressive clown, and the crowd laughed out loud."

Andrew interrupted. "Is this joke going to take long, Martin, 'cos we've got things to deal with?"

"Shut up, Andy, I wanna know the punchline!" said Andreas. "Go on, Martin, go on!"

Martin continued. "Well the little guy left the circus all upset 'cos the clown had made him look a fool. He vowed to get revenge on the clown so he enrolled at university and spent three years doing a degree in 'wit and repartee'! He graduated knowing every literary trick and put down in the book. Then he went back to see the circus! Sure enough, the same clown was performing and sure enough he noticed the little guy again. The lights dimmed and the clown pointed at the little fella again and said:

'Hey, you! Are you a left arse?'

'No.'

'Are you a centre arse?'

'No.'

'Then you must be a right arse'! The clown and the crowd

burst out laughing.

But the little guy remained standing up and stared at the clown. Everyone fell silent as the little fella pointed at the clown and shouted: 'Piss off you red-nosed bastard!'"

For a second everyone thought about the punchline and Martin began to think the joke might fail. But slowly the words sunk in and general laughter filled the room.

"Can we get back on track, please?" implored Andrew, beginning to wonder if Scott of the Antarctic had experienced this sort of trouble. No wonder Captain Oates had walked away saying: "I'm going and I may be some time."

"That's not bad, Martin! I mean three years' study and the best he can do is 'piss off you red-nosed bastard'! Really funny!" said Jeremy, pondering on the joke.

"Look, back to tents please! We've got a Wren Senior tent that Andreas, Chris and I can sleep in." Andrew said, keen to get back to more important issues.

Robert looked at Jeremy. "Looks like I'm still looking for a tent. You happy for me to be with you, Jeremy?" A quiet nod from Jeremy settled the final sleeping arrangements.

Andrew continued to hold the floor. "So that's clear then is it? Robert and Jeremy are in Jeremy's tent, Joe and Martin are together in the youth club tent and Andreas, Chris and I are in our three-man tent. I hope you've all got good sleeping bags and proper walking boots?"

"Martin, you can wear your ballet shoes," sneered Robert. Yet again the twins locked in combat.

This time, Jeremy refrained from joining the 'twin separating' hiatus and Andrew ended up with a bruised cheek as reward. In the melee, no one noticed Joe munching yet another chocolate biscuit from a heap which looked anything but chocolatey. Interestingly, the entire team did note, but again refrained from mentioning, that Chris was again laughing!

"Thanks for that, Robert!" said a sarcastic Andrew, touching his face with his hand before examining it for traces of blood. "Can we stay focused: anybody got any stuff at home that might be useful?"

"I've got some boxing gloves for the twins," joked Jeremy.

"Good idea," added Andrew, rubbing his face.

"We've got a couple of gas stoves, you know the ones with small blue cylinders that you screw on the bottom," said Chris.

"I've got one of them frying pan and saucepan billycan sets for camping," said Andreas. "Everyone will need a knife, fork and spoon, maybe a plate and tin mug."

"No, you eat out of the saucepan; you know, your billycan kit. It saves washing up," said Chris.

"And it saves weight. We're going to have to watch the amount we're carrying. I'll get one of them billycan kits as well Chris. Come to think of it though, we don't need everyone to carry full saucepan sets!" said Andrew.

"We've got some too," added Robert. "How about everyone else just brings a tin or plastic plate, preferably one that can be either plate or bowl so you don't need to bring both?"

"Good thinking. Look, how about we bring all of this to the next meeting. We've got to be sure everybody's got plates to eat from and that we have the right number of pans and things," added Andrew.

"Food!" yelled out Joe, who had been thinking hard and realising that some essentials were close to his heart. "We've got to make sure we've got dried milk and beans and eggs and stuff."

"Tell you what, why don't you be in charge of finding chocolate biscuits, you seem to be doing bloody well tonight." said Jeremy, pointing to yet another chocolate biscuit Joe had magically extracted out of thin air.

Andrew pulled out a pen and notebook and began to write down some of the suggestions.

"Nobody's mentioned clothes yet," said Jeremy.

"I reckon we should wear clothes!" added Joe, with his usual smile. "It can get really cold on them hills in April; yeah the more I think of it, the more clothes seem like a really, really good idea!"

"Thank you, Joseph, I'll write that down—clothes to be worn, except brown jackets." Andrew added, giving the group a quizzical look.

Martin smiled and added, "Joseph can wear his Amazing Technicolor Dream Coat!"

"Good one, Martin!" replied Joseph. "I've never heard that one before! You're just jealous of my parka with the orange lining!"

"I don't give a rats about your parka mate, I'm getting a Crombie. Well, just as soon as I can afford one anyway!"

"Seriously, chaps, we've got to get the right clothing. Jeans get wet and cold so we need good wet-weather gear and everything we carry needs putting in plastic bags inside our rucksacks in case water leaks in."

"Crikey, we haven't even thought about rucksacks yet!" said Andrew, adding a note to the pad.

"There are some in the youth club!" said Joe.

"Yeah, but they're pretty crappy. They hang too low down your back and hurt your shoulders, I'm going to get a decent one," announced Robert.

"Well, I can't afford that, so I'll bagsie one from the youth club. I'll just have to get something soft, a sponge or something to make the straps feel better," said Joe forlornly.

Andrew kept things focused. "Right, can we meet again in

two weeks? That's only going to leave a bit over a week before we go. Bring your tents, boots, rucksacks and cutlery – in fact bring everything you want to take, including spare clothes and some torches. I'll get some dried milk and grab some cereal. Actually, we should list what food we need and all bring something, so we spread the cost and the weight. Go on, throw a list of food at me and I'll write it all down."

"Steak and chips!" yelled Robert.

"Sensible food that won't go off and that we can carry!" snapped back Andrew, still annoyed with Robert after the brown jacket taunts and the bash to his face.

"I suggested food earlier and you took no notice of me did you! Am I invisible or something?" asked Joseph, aggrieved his food suggestion earlier had been so lightly breezed over.

On that remark, a quick-witted Martin walked across the room and deliberately bashed into Joe, nearly knocking him out of his seat. "Sorry Joe, sorry, I just couldn't see you! Amazing that! I just couldn't see you mate!"

Once everyone had recovered from Martin's latest quip they all began chipping in with ideas of food to be carried: tea, sugar, bacon, eggs, butter, jam, chocolate and bread.

"We need a kitty!" Jeremy excitedly announced.

"Who's going to carry cat food, Jeremy?" joked Martin.

"As long as it sleeps in your tent, Jeremy, that's OK by me!" a jovial Joe added.

"Typical, just typical!" exclaimed Martin.

"What's up with you, Mart?" enquired Chris.

"Just bloody typical that any pussy ends up in Robert's tent!" Martin added with a smile on his face.

Andreas was quick into the fray, producing one of his TV quotes, this time from *Are You Being Served?* "Oh, Mr Humphries, leave my pussy alone!"

When the laughter had settled down, Jeremy continued.

"You know what I mean! We can all put a couple of quid into a kitty to buy the items we're going to share. I'm quite happy to take charge of it, just so long as everyone plays fair and doesn't leave me out of pocket."

"That's good, just so long as you play fair and don't leave us out of pocket!" the ever careful Joe added.

In the end, everyone went home vowing to get organised and ready for the last meeting.

It was decided that the final meeting would be in a fort-night's time at Andrew's place. An air of excitement existed and everyone began to get the feeling that something memora-ble was beginning to take shape.

Andrew Price no longer looked or felt bored. Such feelings were replaced with glorious anticipation.

Chapter 4

The Final Meeting

Chris, Andrew and Andreas went shopping at a large camping store in Nottingham. Chris didn't have to spend much because he already had wet-weather gear, a rucksack, boots and sleeping bag, but he came along to offer advice.

The first thing Andrew purchased was a large yellow rucksack with upper and lower compartments. The rucksack was carried fairly high up on the back and had external, zipped, pockets on the sides. At the base was a fold out metal frame for supporting a tent. Next on the shopping list was a sleeping bag, followed by some hiking boots with firm leather uppers to prevent spraining ankles on rough ground. The latter was purchased on sound advice from Chris's safety-conscious dad. Some thick, warm socks, a cutlery set and a clip-together saucepan set completed Andrew's purchases. The saucepan set was a beauty with a detachable handle that also served as a support for the frying pan. All the pans doubled as either plate or bowl.

Andreas also got a sleeping bag, some boots and camping cutlery and a set of fluorescent orange wet-weather trousers with matching jacket. He also obtained a small, but powerful, torch.

On the way home on the bus, the three young men looked like real explorers in the making, or at least that's what they thought they looked like. In truth, they must have looked the part because a man seated opposite looked at them and said: "Where you off to then, lads? You going to climb Mount Everest?"

Andrew smiled appropriately and replied: "Not that adventurous, I'm afraid. We're going to walk the Cleveland Way. It's a long distance walking track round the North York Moors."

"Well make sure you take care – watch out for Yorkshiremen!" was the man's witty reply.

Joseph went on a borrowing expedition to the youth club. The dreaded low-hung rucksack was acquired, plus a tin plate, a plastic mug and a useful folding trowel. The youth club organiser assured him the trowel would be necessary in case any of the group got 'caught short' high on the moors and miles from a toilet. The latter was promptly tied to the back of Joe's rucksack so as to be immediately available to everyone. He borrowed cutlery from home and also purloined his older brother's sleeping bag. It would have been borrowed, but Joe's brother, Paul, was at university and Joseph just hoped he wouldn't notice it was missing from the wardrobe in the hall. He also got the youth club tent, which felt very heavy. It had all the features, like a sewn-in ground sheet and extra space for rucksacks, but it definitely felt heavy. Still, he didn't have to carry it all as Martin, his 'room-mate' on the walk, would have to take half of it.

Chris gathered his gear together, again borrowing from family members where he had to. He purchased his allocation of foodstuffs and remembered to buy a couple of gas cylinders to power the little gas stoves he was bringing along. He also got matches, of the safety variety naturally, in a special waterproof container.

Jeremy decided to erect the family two-man tent on the back lawn, just to make sure everything was present and correct. It was a good thing he did because there were no tent poles! An extensive house search located them in the garage, so all was complete. Jeremy also purchased some of the longer lasting food items on his list. Things such as dried milk, a cereal variety pack, jam, sugar and tea bags were accumulated for the next meeting. He also studied the list of perishable foods, which would need getting the day the walk began, and to this list he added a block of cheese and some apples.

The twins already had sleeping bags and boots. A trip to town saw them with wet-weather gear of a particularly colourful and high-visibility variety. They also purchased rucksacks. Two Karrimor Totem Pack Seniors to be precise. A matching pair, for a matching pair. When the twins were out walking on the hills in their identical wet-weather clothing and carrying identical rucksacks, telling them apart was going to be hard work, even for those who had known them a long time. There was going to be one difference, however. Robert purchased for himself a plastic map container and a Silva compass. He was determined to be the group's map reader and, as he now possessed a waterproof holder for the map, his position was assured. The twins also purchased a small torch each and some foodstuffs. Some for the group and some for themselves.

Slowly but surely things were coming together. On the evening of the last meeting, just a week before the walk began, the would-be explorers began to arrive at Andrew's home. One by one the members of the group, along with all their equipment, gathered in the garage.

First to arrive was Jeremy with an old-looking rucksack packed full of stuff. The tent wasn't even packed in it yet as Jeremy needed to share the load with Robert Jenkins. A strange sweet smell accompanied Jeremy's entrance, which Andrew Price immediately recognised.

"You've had fish and chips for tea, haven't you?" postulated Andrew.

"No, not today," said a bemused Jeremy.

"Well, you smell like you've just had fish and chips," said Andrew, realizing the smell was incredibly powerful.

"No, that's the vinegar I've been soaking my feet in," said Jeremy, in a tone that made soaking your feet in vinegar seem like something normal and commonplace.

"Why would you do that then?" asked Andrew. "Is it something to do with the band? Does it make you sing more tunefully or something?"

"Soaking your feet in vinegar makes your feet go hard and stops blisters. Didn't you ever play conkers?" Jeremy asked.

"What's playing conkers got to do with it?" Andrew asked incredulously.

"You soak conkers in vinegar to make 'em go hard so you win more and it's the same with feet. If you soak feet in vinegar you get less blisters, your skin gets more resilient," an utterly convinced Jeremy replied.

Andrew was a little doubtful: "Well, all I can say is, I've never heard of it."

The twins pulled up in the Jenkins' spare car with Joe in the back. They got out and opened the boot, revealing three rucksacks full to overflowing with equipment. They also carried several rolled up sleeping bags that so far didn't have a home. They proceeded to haul their pile of camping gear into the garage.

Joe was first to speak, sniffing the air and looking straight at Andrew.

"Crikey, don't tell me we're not having chocolate biscuits tonight but you've got us all fish and chips!"

Andrew pointed to Jeremy and replied: "No, it's Jeremy."

Joseph gave Jeremy a suitable 'food gatherers' smile' and asked: "You've brought us all fish and chips, Jez? Hey that's really great!"

"You'll have to say Grace, Joe," Robert added.

"Where are they then? I mean, we've got to eat 'em! We can't pack 'em for the trip, can we?" commented Martin, drooling at the prospect of some chips.

An embarrassed Jeremy quietly pointed downwards and said: "It's vinegar on me feet, to make 'em go hard. You know, like conkers!"

The twins looked at him nonplussed and replied in unison: "You what?"

Any further inquiry was thwarted by the arrival of Andreas and Chris in Mr Hewson's Volvo estate. They climbed out of the car carrying two well-packed rucksacks, which, unlike the rest of the group, seemed to have room to spare. Mr Hewson also emerged and walked purposefully into the garage with his well-known look of serious concern.

"So, you're all going to do this then? Have you got a first aid kit? Have you got a plan if one of you gets injured?" He paused and sniffed the air.

"What's that incredibly strong acid smell, have you got something wrong with a gas stove or something?"

"No, sir," said Andrew, reverting to classroom terminology and addressing Mr Hewson in the manner he was accustomed to in history class. "No, sir, it's Jeremy, he's put vinegar on his feet to harden them up for the walk. You know, like conkers."

Mr Hewson looked at Jeremy with the hint of a smile, the same sort of smile he had had when the woodwork teacher fainted at school.

"Well I've heard it all now. Vinegar, hey? Actually lads, in the First World War to stop callouses and blisters they used to urinate on their feet and, you know what, I don't reckon it'd smell much different! Brilliant lad, brilliant!"

"Will vinegar actually work though, Dad, you know, to stop blisters?" Chris enquired.

"No idea! It's an interesting experiment! For those who want a well tried and tested solution can I suggest you simply wear two pairs of socks when you're walking. Put a thin pair on first, then your walking socks. What happens is the two layers of socks chafe together instead of layers of skin. The end result is no blisters! Dead easy and you don't have to smell like a fish and chip shop after somebody's dropped the vinegar bottle!"

Mr Hewson finished his address to Jeremy and turned to Andrew.

"Your dad's taking you on this expedition isn't he? I'd like a quick word with him before I go please, Andrew, but let me say this to all of you..." Mr Hewson turned to address the entire group, "Well done for getting off your backsides and taking this on. I'm impressed with you, but make sure you're safe. All of you should know where your friends' home phone numbers are, have some change for the phone box ready, don't use gas cookers inside your tents because carbon monoxide could build up, don't get silly near cliff edges, be safe crossing roads and look after each other. Yes, yes, well done. Be careful and, and, and... I look forward to hearing about it when you get back! Right, Andrew, your dad, please!"

Andrew Price led Mr Hewson off to have a chat with his father, leaving everyone else contemplating how to distribute piles of gear.

Robert spoke first: "Right, gather round everybody!"

A smiling Joe asked: "Why, are we going to piss on Jeremy's feet?"

Andreas was quick to respond. "No we're going to piss on

yours so we've got a proper biological experiment with you and Jeremy as the 'treatments' and the rest of us as 'controls' with nothing applied to our feet except walking socks." Andreas was pleased to see today's experimental biology lesson put, so quickly, to a practical use.

Robert followed on. "No, let's gather round and share out all the stuff we've got to jointly carry and then look at the extra stuff we've all brought along, 'cos some of these rucksacks look way too heavy already."

"Way too heavy! – weigh too heavy! Get it?" laughed Joe, who enjoyed playing with words and making corny jokes.

"Shut up, Joe! Right, find a space everybody and let's unpack and see what everyone's got in their bags," said Robert, who was enjoying taking control in the absence of Andrew. Really, Andrew was only leader by default and solely by virtue of having suggested the idea of walking the Cleveland Way in the first place. Interestingly, everyone in the group had leadership potential, so it was going to be intriguing to see how the group would function and whether tempers would become frayed as individuals vied for position and authority.

Andrew returned from delivering Mr Hewson to his father. He had hung around long enough to realise Mr Hewson was doing his safety bit, asking Mr Price all about the walk the seven intrepid explorers were about to embark upon and making sure everything sounded organised and safe.

In the garage, equipment was being disgorged from rucksacks. Martin was halfway through unpacking his haversack when a medium-sized teddy bear rolled on to the floor. This was the moment his brother Robert had been waiting for. Ten minutes before leaving home Robert had deliberately hidden the bear in Martin's bag.

Robert pointed and said: "You haven't got room for your

teddy bear, Mart, I told you that before we left home!"

"But I never put it in there," said a puzzled Martin before realization crossed his face and it was all on again. Martin launched himself at Robert in another flurry of flailing fists, only ended by Andreas and Jeremy, who managed to hold him back. This time no one got hurt, but kit got scattered everywhere, much to Andrew's annoyance.

"For crying out loud you two, will you pack in fighting, it's driving us all crazy," he complained loudly.

"It's not my fault, it's him, the red-nosed bastard!" said Martin, pointing at his sneering brother.

For some reason, Chris was wetting himself laughing in the corner of the garage.

"Let's share out the joint equipment then," said Andrew, reasserting control. An action made all the easier by Robert's practical joke on his brother, which was something everyone was plainly getting bored with. Except for Chris, of course, who could obviously see a funny side no one else was aware of!

"Everyone needs one full spare set of clothes, preferably kept in their rucksack in one of these plastic bags," said Andrew, passing out some thick clear plastic bags his dad used for selling liquid egg to bakeries in Nottingham.

Andreas and Chris had their sleeping bags already rolled tightly in plastic bags on top of their rucksacks. This placed the weight high up and left heaps of room in their bags. They pointed this idea out and the method was universally adopted.

Jeremy mentioned his experiences with his tent and the missing tent poles. This caused immediate panic and the other two tents were hastily unpacked and checked over. Everything was present and correct and so the great share out could occur. This went surprisingly easily, with those occupying a particular tent taking their share of the load.

As Andrew, Andreas and Chris were all in the same tent, these three did seem to get off lightly when it came to division of weight, something not missed by the others. To even things out, those in the three-man tent agreed to carry extra food.

Chris was keen to demonstrate his camping stoves and proceeded to screw a blue gas cylinder to the burner part of the apparatus. He fumbled and dropped a punctured blue cylinder, issuing copious amounts of liquefied gas on to the garage floor. This was the first crisis faced by the group and the initial reaction was one of 'statue panic'. Basically, everybody stood still and stared in horror at the escaping gas.

Chris was first to speak and simply said: "Dad's going to love this!" But almost as he spoke, Andreas leapt into action. Like Heracles himself, Andreas grabbed the cylinder and threw it into the garden as if it were a hand grenade about to explode. The silence in the garage was only broken by Chris who, strangely, began to laugh!

Joe finally decided to broach what had been, until now, a taboo subject. He turned to Chris and asked the question that was on everybody's lips.

"What's funny about that then? You know, I'm getting seriously worried about you! I'm glad I don't have to sleep in the same tent as you! Hey you lot, if you hear him laughing late at night for goodness sake go and look in his tent. Some poor sod will probably be lying there with an axe in their head or something!"

"What's that meant to mean, Joseph?" Chris enquired.

"It means you seem to laugh at stuff that isn't funny, mate," Joe replied. "When you watch a horror film, or an action-packed war film, do you sit there laughing? I wouldn't be surprised!"

Martin brought on a change of subject by congratulating Andreas for his swift action. He said it for everyone by slapping

Andreas on the back and saying: "Good on ya, Zorba. You've saved the day!"

"Yeah, well done, 'Dreas," added Andrew and Jeremy.

Robert undertook the task of setting up another stove and, after waiting for the smell of gas to disappear, lit it just to make sure it worked.

"Don't worry, I'll get a couple more cylinders," Chris promised.

Next the group started checking that all the various shaped cooking pans in their possession fitted on to the gas stoves.

"You know what, Chris, I reckon we're going to need a couple more stoves," Andrew said, worried that when the entire group were preparing a meal it was going to take too long using the small number of appliances in their possession. Joe came to the rescue, promising that he would grab a couple of stoves from the youth club that were exactly the same type.

It was time for a trial pack of the rucksacks. Bit by bit everything was packed into the haversacks and miraculously it all went in. They were just short of being full so there was still room for some of the more perishable foods, which were to be purchased on the way up to Helmsley on Monday. There was, however, quite a lot left behind; several heavy coats, spare shoes, a transistor radio and even an inflatable lilo, which Jeremy had hoped he would have room for to use as a mattress, were among the discarded items. Everyone had realised that light, wet-weather gear was all that could be carried for inclement weather. There was certainly no room for cumbersome duffel coats. Those who had brought large bath towels vowed to change them for lightweight hand towels and just make do if ever the luxury of a bath or shower presented itself during the expedition.

The ultimate sacrifice was made by Andreas, who opened his small bag of toiletries and took out his toothbrush. With a flourish he snapped the handle in half.

"See, that saves me some weight, and I'm taking a half full tube of toothpaste, not a full one!"

Martin smiled at him. "If we all use both sides of each piece of toilet paper we needn't carry as much of that either! What do you reckon, 'Dreas?" This comment brought general laughter from the group.

"You may well laugh, fellas," said Joe, "but I've been reading about the Second World War and the allowance for toilet paper for British servicemen was a measly three pieces per day! The allowance for American soldiers was twenty-two!"

"Dad always said the American army was full of big arse-holes. I never realised he meant it so literally!" Jeremy added.

"Apparently, the first piece of paper was to clean, the second to dry and the third to shine things up!" said Joe with a beaming smile!

"Well, it's all very well trying to make small items lighter," added Robert, thoughtfully, "but there's something heavy we have forgotten. Water! We'll have to carry water! We can't rely on finding clean water, not to drink, and we're bound to get thirsty when we're walking!"

Jeremy backed him up. "He's right, we'll all have to get some sort of water bottle, either proper camping ones, or plastic orange juice containers or something."

With a flourish, Chris opened a side pocket on his rucksack and produced a small packet. "These are water purification tablets. Dad got them for us. If we ever have to drink from a mountain stream or river you just add one of these and it kills the bugs before you swallow the water." The pack of small white chlorine tablets was passed around to genuine interest from all assembled. However, the consensus was that everyone needed to carry their own drinking water and that somehow they would find a tap with potable water near their campsites to cook with, wash with and replenish drinking water for the next day's hike. The water purification tablets would accompany them but would only be used in an emergency.

Finally, all the bags were packed and everyone began to experiment with carrying them. At this point, the fancy shovel tied to Joe's bag was noticed for the first time by Robert.

"Hey, Joe, you hoping to do some gardening or something, I mean who's carrying the seeds!"

Joe gave him a scornful glance before explaining to the group the true function of the 'burying shovel'. An explanation that was well received by all and allowed Andrew to deliver an environmental lecture on how nobody was to leave litter, or kill any wildlife or leave gates open. All good stuff, but everybody had heard Andrew on this topic before and, frankly, he could be nauseating with his do-good environmental preaching!

"Maybe we should eat hedgehogs or bird's eggs?" suggested Robert, slipping easily into 'piss-take' mode.

"Yeah, I'm not going to bury my poo," added Martin. "I'm just going to leave it lying around as a sort of marker just to prove I've been there!"

Robert was warming to the subject. "Yeah, in the guidebook it says we have to climb a hill called Roseberry Topping. Well, I'm going to make sure I need to go on the very top and leave a sort of steaming cairn on the summit!"

All this teasing would stop if Andrew just ignored it but, ever the gullible, he believed everything said and continued to preach a responsible approach to countryside management.

"You just can't do that, what about those who come after you? It's just not on, the English countryside is under a lot of pressure and we've got to cherish everywhere we go and pick up our litter, and above all, bury our poo!"

The conversation was brought to an end, however, by the return of Mr Hewson and Andrew's dad.

"You lads ready for home then? We're dropping Jeremy off on the way, his mum just phoned." Mr Hewson grabbed one of the laden rucksacks. "These don't feel too bad," he added, lifting his son's rucksack into the car.

"It's not surprising, Dad, because we've all left heaps out, they're too heavy otherwise," Chris replied.

Mike Price raised his voice, explaining the pick-up route on the Monday coming.

"Right, we'll be leaving here at six in the morning. Chris and Andreas will have to be here by then because we don't go near their homes on the way to Helmsley."

Mr Hewson assured Mike he would have Chris and Andreas at the Price residence by 6am.

Mike continued: "Right then, we can pick up the twins and Jeremy, then lastly you, Joseph, on the way to the A1. So please be ready by twenty past six. Get a good breakfast, because it'll probably be your last decent meal for a week or so!" He paused to laugh at his own joke not really aware of how well the youth club had prepared the assembled young men in the art of preparing camp cuisine. Not that they were gourmet cooks, or anything, but they certainly weren't going to go hungry!

"Remember, as you go round the Cleveland Way you must let me know how things are going. It's no use getting to Filey and then ringing and expecting me to drop everything to come and pick you up. I need fair warning, you know, a day or so in advance."

Assurances were given that regular phone calls would keep their families informed of progress. Finally, everyone dispersed. They were as ready as they ever would be. Roll on Monday, April 8th, 1974!!

Chapter 5

Onward to Helmsley

The week passed in a flurry of activity for all the team. Last-minute changes were made, usually in a frantic effort to reduce the weight of their haversacks. Everyone had a secret stash of money generously donated by parents, who, on the one hand, wanted to make sure their offspring were able to survive the week to ten days it was estimated the walk would take, but on the other hand were keen to subsidise a period of freedom from their teenage sons. Not having sixteen and seventeen year old teenagers hanging around home during the Easter holidays was, frankly, an anticipated relief for all the parents, so a bit of extra money handed out to the boys was considered a good investment to ensure a restful Easter period.

The last school week before Easter seemed to drag. It was, nevertheless, a memorable one for Andreas, Andrew and Chris. Maybe it was the prospect of the walk, or maybe just a stage Andreas was going through, but he seemed particularly cheerful and humorous. One of the science teachers at Melton Upper School was, at that time, a woman of exceptional 'nun-like' demeanour. She wore country-style tweeds with thick woollen leggings. Her hair was unkempt and she appeared elderly and severe. She spoke in a squeaky monotone, which straightaway caused her pupils to lose the will to live, let alone learn anything. Miss Rogers was a single lady. This was not surprising to male pupils with even limited relationship experience. The general opinion was she would forever remain in that condition. In short, it was considered she was likely to be as frigid as a fridge door!

All the more amusing then, was the geography lesson where Andreas caused the laugh of the year.

The radiators in the old part of the upper school were of the old cast iron pipe variety and the plumbing was prone to air locks. During an intense study period in geography, where Andreas, Andrew, Chris and all the other pupils were busy copying down all the locations in the USA where coal was mined, the radiators began to rattle and shake. This went on for a good minute, in a vigorous manner far worse than usual. Finally, the cacophony came to an abrupt stop and almost immediately Andreas piped up:

"It's all right everyone, it's only Miss Rogers' vibrator!"

The entire classroom was in hilarious uproar. Even the teacher, a young, newly graduated, intense and firm member of staff, was seen to have tears rolling down his face, as he too couldn't help but join in the mirth.

The other four members of the walking seven didn't share subjects in quite such an intimate way, although the twins were usually to be seen in each other's company. The major concern that Jeremy, Robert and Martin shared related to the performance their band Dutch Courage was booked to give on Friday night at Scalford village hall. Practise had been difficult as their minds were not in music mode but instead were preoccupied with the forthcoming walk.

Robert had the distraction of a very pretty girl in youth club called Ruth. This particular young lady was totally and utterly in love with Robert, who was without doubt the 'alpha male' of the club. Robert on the other hand, was half-hearted with his feelings of love, except of course when it came to long sessions of snogging in the garage belonging to the girl's family. Ruth's parents would often enquire as to whether the 'garage attendant' was coming over tonight. Usually, they would give them half an hour or so of 'heavy petting' before opening the door from the kitchen and then acting surprised when Robert was still there. Just enough interruption to prevent their beloved daughter from joining the statistics of teenage pregnancy and just enough to prevent Robert from experiencing the full extent of pleasure that such unions can provide! Nevertheless, it did mean Robert was the most sexually experienced of the seven young men about to embark on a different type of manly initiation. Even though Joseph Krinn had a girlfriend, matters relating to the female form were generally addressed to Robert, who sounded and acted like a professional in all matters relating to women.

Friday night arrived and the band found themselves setting up for their performance. The usual checks on equipment hadn't taken place, resulting in Martin failing to pack the lead for his guitar. Derek had to drive the butcher's van back as fast as he could for Martin to get it, but by the time they got back the large group of gathered girls were getting very impatient. So it was to a slightly hostile audience, that Jeremy started singing 'Bony Moronie'. So flustered was he that he promptly forgot the words! By half-time most of the girls had left, the only ones remaining were those waiting for parents to taxi them home. Dutch courage had experienced a seriously bad night. Ten o'clock came and the boys couldn't wait to get home and turn their thoughts back to the challenge ahead of them.

Joseph was having a tumultuous time with Yvonne. It was clear to him that she didn't want him to go away with his mates – not that she could expect to see much of him over the Easter period anyway, as any visits Joe made involved the long haul to

Melton. This wouldn't be too bad normally, but it so happened that Joe's moped was out of action. Visiting Yvonne at home would involve several miles walking to Long Clawson to catch the Melton bus and several miles walking home in the dark when the last bus deposited him in Clawson again. It appeared to Joe that Yvonne was trying to impose an unreasonable level of control on him at this stage of his life but he did confide to Martin that he loved her dearly (as if he didn't already know!) and he really didn't want to lose her because of the walk.

The school week finished, the band's abysmal performance consigned to history and the Sunday before the walk all but over, found all members of the walking group busy making final adjustments. Repacking their rucksacks, cleaning their walking boots with dubbin and secreting extra food items into their packs.

Finally, bedtime approached, alarms were set and the seven hikers, in various locations in north-east Leicestershire, drifted off to sleep. All of them were experiencing apprehension and excitement as they contemplated the next ten days or so.

Mike didn't have to get his son out of bed on Monday, April 8th. Quite the opposite to the previous two days when Andrew had been working on the chicken farm collecting eggs. No, today Andrew was up before the alarm had even rung. Mrs Price made sure her eldest son left for his adventure with a proper breakfast. After porridge was the inevitable boiled egg – something not unexpected on an egg producing poultry farm!

Mike Price had organised the farm to function without him on the morning he was acting as a taxi service. This was an almost unheard of occurrence as it was difficult to find staff willing to take on the skilful poultry checking and intricate feeding routines. The old Transit van had been checked over and filled with fuel. It even sparkled a bit thanks to a quick squirt with the pressure washer.

All too soon, Mr Hewson arrived with Chris and Andreas.

"Throw your bags in the back of the van," Mike yelled to them. "Then hop in yourselves. I've put an old mattress and lots of pillows in the back for you to sit on 'cos we've quite a long way to go."

Mr Hewson gave another impromptu lecture on looking after each other and the importance of phoning home. Andrew's mum rushed out to wave them off as the Transit drove out of the yard. Andrew had the comfort of the passenger seat, while Chris and Andreas lay on the mattress in the back of the van.

Jeremy, who lived close to the twins, was waiting with them when the van arrived.

"I've just walked half a mile," Jeremy exclaimed. "I'm knackered already!"

Along with Andreas and Chris, Jeremy and the twins piled into the back of the van. Their rucksacks were heaped to one side.

"Don't fart, Robert," said Martin.

"Don't tell me he farts!" said Jeremy. "Please don't tell me he farts 'cos I'm in his tent!"

"No farting in the van please, or you're walking the Cleveland Way from here!" Mike pointed out, not wanting to drive for the next two and a half hours in a smelly van.

The van pulled away but almost immediately Robert was craning his neck to see out the side window with an inquisitive look on his face. "She's going to wave me goodbye as we go past the church."

Mike glanced at him and asked. "Who is?"

"Ruth, my girlfriend! I went over to her place and said goodbye last night, but that's not good enough apparently. Now she wants me to wave as well."

"Well that's fair enough, Rob, 'cos I don't reckon sticking your tongue down her throat counts as saying goodbye!" said Jeremy, somewhat jealous that Robert had a female who loved him enough to get herself out of bed at this time of day just to say cheerio.

As they drove towards the church, a diminutive female figure could be seen in the bus shelter.

"Do you want me to stop?" asked Mike.

"No, he's used all his condoms!" announced Martin. "And besides, I don't want to watch him fondling Ruth at this time of day." Much to everyone's surprise, and maybe because an adult was present, this remark went unavenged and just for once the twins didn't resort to full combat.

"No, I'll just give her a wave," said Robert.

As they approached, everyone gathered around the front seats to witness Robert give a small wave to a pretty young girl crying her eyes out and waving vigorously next to the shelter.

"Don't leave me, Robert. Come back darling, I love you!" could be heard plainly as the van passed by.

Jeremy summed up the situation. "Bloody hell, Rob, she's got it bad!"

"She's not pregnant is she, Rob?" asked his twin brother, who yet again got away with a comment that would usually elicit some form of violence.

Robert just smiled, turned and sat down, as if this was quite a normal reaction from the female of the species.

"Well, at least you know that back home somebody's thinking about you, don't you, Rob," added Chris. This comment saw the group erupt into song, giving a hearty rendition of the England football squad's number one hit of 1970 entitled 'Back Home'.

Joe was waiting outside the family home with an over-effusive and protective mother. She stuck her head in the back of the Transit van, realised someone had indeed farted, and retreated slightly before imploring Mike to drive carefully. She then turned to her much-loved son Joseph and begged him to keep in touch. The van drove off, with both side windows wound down, to the sound of Mrs Krinn shouting "God bless and safe journey". As her calls receded, the group again sang 'back home they'll be thinking about us' just to make Joe squirm. Naturally, it had no effect on him at all.

It was 6.35am and the journey had begun.

Mike Price knew where he was going. Being a Yorkshireman, all Mike's vehicles automatically turned towards 'God's own county' the moment any journey began. He took the road north from the village of Harby towards Bingham, then over the Trent at 'Gunthorpe and toilets' on the A6097. It was really just Gunthorpe but the sign just across the Trent actually said 'Gunthorpe and toilets'! Every time the Price family headed north this was read out by Mr Price and it always caused great amusement, no matter how many times it happened!

"If I was writing a letter to anyone in Gunthorpe, I'd put 'Gunthorpe and toilets' as the address, just for a laugh," was Mr Price's usual, but still funny, comment.

The journey to Helmsley continued northwards from 'Gunthorpe and toilets' and on to the A614, before joining the A1 at the big roundabout which used to be just north of Clumber Park. Mike then followed the Great North Road until their first stop at a service area just south of Castleford. The rush for the toilets saw a stream of young men frantically dash from the back of the Transit when Andrew opened the doors.

"About flamin' time," said an anguished Joe, who had been begging for a toilet break for the past half hour.

The weather was reasonable, not raining, but overcast and

grey. The temperature was also reasonable, not too cold and not too hot – just right for the much anticipated start of the walk.

With the van re-loaded with its passengers, the journey continued to the strains of T. Rex and Gary Glitter on the radio. When the Nancy Sinatra song 'These Boots are Made for Walkin'' came on it seemed very appropriate and the 'professional band members' joined in with full force. Much to Jeremy's delight, this was followed by the Mixtures and their 'Pushbike' song.

"Using bikes is what we should be doing, we'd be done much quicker!" he announced.

"We'd never carry all this gear on our bikes, and besides, we're doing the Cleveland Way, remember. That's cross country paths and rocky scrambles – bikes would never do it." Andrew was quick to point out the obvious failings of attempting the Cleveland Way walking track on bicycles.

"I was joking! I'd sorta guessed we were a bit late to change," said a sarcastic Jeremy.

Chris instigated a discussion on football, which was shared by Mike, Jeremy and Martin. All were interested in the upcoming game between Sheffield United and Liverpool. Chris was firmly of the opinion that Liverpool would triumph, but would still not catch Leeds in the race to win the league title. Both teams had won their Saturday games and so the two-horse race for the top spot in division one was still being fought.

Mike left the A1 at Boroughbridge and began his favourite bit of the trip, cross country through small villages including Sessay. Just round the corner from Sessay was his cousin's farm, which Mike was going to visit after he had got rid of the hikers. The journey passed close to the White Horse of Kilburn, through Coxwold, past the ruins of Byland Abbey and up on to the hills above Sutton Bank to join a short section of the A170, as it descended into Helmsley.

"I take it you all realise you'll soon be walking next to the White Horse?" asked Mike. "The Cleveland Way walks right along that ridge – looks good doesn't it!"

A silence spread over the seven as they contemplated the adventure to come. Those who could see out of the van began to look for landmarks. Martin, on his knees behind the passenger seat, was first to see the gaunt ruins of Helmsley Castle protruding through leafless trees on the left. Finally, the old Transit pulled into the quaint market square marking the centre of Helmsley. The van pulled up in front of the old Market Cross, which is the official start point of the Cleveland Way. An elderly man gave the occupants of the Transit a wave from the dubious comfort of the time-worn steps he was sitting on. Steps that circled the Market Cross. The wave was returned by Mike Price and the young men in the front of the vehicle.

With the engine turned off, a strange silence descended over the group. It was as if everyone was reluctant to commit to making a start. Contemplating what was about to occur had rendered all those present strangely speechless. The silence was broken by Mike Price.

"Well, I'm not driving back with you lot left in the back! Come on all of you, get cracking. You've got a real challenge in front of you! Come on, move it!"

Andrew went around the back and opened the rear doors of the van. He was greeted by Joe, who uttered the first words spoken by the seven on the Cleveland Way. Prophetic words that most of the seven would utter at some stage on the walk, but nevertheless words most often said by Joe.

"Where's the toilet then? I'm bursting!"

Chapter 6

Helmsley to Sneck Yate Bank

Slowly and stiffly, the hikers emerged from the back of the van, several running off after Joe to the public lavatories over to one side of the town centre. Mike Price helped drag rucksacks out on to the road and lined them up alongside the vehicle. He then carried out his own cardboard box containing four large thermos flasks and some egg sandwiches made earlier by Andrew's mother.

"Here you go, lads, here's a quick snack to start you off." Everyone grabbed a sandwich, a cup of tea and a couple of chocolate biscuits. It was a quarter past nine in the morning, the sun was breaking through and a feeling of anticipation was in the air.

In addition to the large yellow rucksack, with bits of tent attached beneath and a rolled up sleeping bag in a plastic bag tied on top, Andrew also had his dad's 10x50 binoculars round his neck and the Cleveland Way guidebook in his hand. The binoculars were heavy, but birdwatching would be difficult without them and who knows what new species would be added to Andrew's tally on this trip. In one of the rucksack side pockets Andrew carried a Collins book entitled *The Birds of Britain and Europe*. This field guide with its maps showing the winter, summer and resident range of more than 650 bird species was like a Bible for Andrew. Especially now that he had out-grown the little *Observer's Book of Birds* he used to carry. The main disadvantage was the extra weight, as this book was quite a bit larger than its predecessor.

Robert Jenkins had the map, opened to display the start of the Cleveland Way, hanging around his neck in the clear plastic map holder he had purchased only last week. He also sported a white bandanna, or sweat band, on his head in an effort to appear that bit 'cooler' than the rest of the group. Robert had already surveyed the Market Place and was very keen to locate the actual start point of the walk.

"On the map it shows the start of the walk next to the church, which must mean it's up there somewhere," he said, gesturing towards the street over by the churchyard.

Joseph helped Martin on with his 'top heavy' rucksack and Martin reciprocated by helping Joe on with his 'bottom heavy' one.

"Here, Mart, just push these sponges under the straps as I lift and 'utch the bag up to make room for them." Joe was struggling to get organised and looked the least fashionable, with an old-fashioned haversack hanging low and a parka coat tied around his waist because he simply hadn't been able to afford wet-weather clothing of the lightweight/high-visibility variety. The sponges were a last-minute find by his mother and meant she would need to go shopping before being able to wash the kitchen lino again!

Joe looked around and noticed Andrew with the guidebook.

"Here Andrew, give us the book a minute. I just want to read about the castle and get a feel for the history of this place." Joe took the book for a while to refresh his memory of the district.

"There's not that much about the castle in this book but it is thirteenth century!" he announced, handing the book back to Andrew. "There's loads on Rievaulx Abbey, though, and old mines and folklore. Hey, and guess what?! William Wordsworth spent time around here with his wife! Maybe I'll be inspired to write a poem to Yvonne! Let's see:

I walk through hills and valleys to lay down by your
    side,
You look sublime and beautiful
Oh Yvonne, please be my bride!!"
Martin, ever the wit was quick to respond:
"My hair is long, my pack is heavy,
I go down on bended knee.
Not to propose, oh beautiful, Yvonne!
But because again, I need to pee!!"

"Thanks, Martin! Thanks a lot!" said Joe, secretly wondering what Yvonne was doing and whether she was missing him or not.

Jeremy, Andreas and Chris emerged from a local shop. They had been tasked with buying bread and bacon, two of the perishable items the group had vowed to purchase *en route*. Jeremy, being the expedition's treasurer, was carrying the kitty and as such took charge of group purchases. With the foodstuffs stowed in the spaces within Chris and Andreas's rucksacks, their loads were hoisted on to their backs.

Finally, everyone was loaded up and the walk could commence. Mike took out his camera and photographed the group, who appeared fresh, clean and excited. "Off you go then. Good luck and keep in touch," were Mike's parting words.

"This way then fellas," said Robert, taking the lead. With the church on the right, the group took its first faltering steps.

"The book says we are to go up the lane marked 'footpath to Rievaulx'," said Andrew, studiously examining the guidebook.

Sure enough, there stood the sign proclaiming 'footpath to Rievaulx', pointing up a street aptly named Cleveland Way.

Robert, who was reading from notes on the map, added: "We've to look out for acorns on posts – you know markers. Look, here's the first one." Sure enough, on a post next to a stile was a small white acorn insignia. All seven proceeded to take turns climbing over the stile with varying degrees of success. The most annoying part was catching tent poles or protruding sleeping bags on the side posts. As the walk continued west, several more stiles presented themselves and so, slowly but surely, the group was able to practise and perfect techniques of climbing them while fully laden. The track gained elevation with Helmsley Castle protruding above the trees in the south-east. The route continued westwards along a well-defined track before crossing to the south towards woodland.

"Hang about fellas, can you hear that?" asked Andrew, his ear tuned for bird noises.

Chris turned and replied sarcastically: "Don't tell us – you've seen a bird."

"I've seen no end but haven't bothered you with anything yet," snapped back Andrew.

"Go on then, what have you seen so far?" asked Martin, who had a passing interest in birds.

"Well, so far I've seen jackdaws in the town; chaffinch, great tit, dunnock, house sparrow, robin, wood pigeon and blackbird. But they're not as exciting as this. Listen, can't you hear it?"

The track was passing alongside a wooded slope. From deep within the trees could be heard a 'queu, queu, queu' sound, almost like laughter but more regular and melodic. "What is it then?" asked Chris, somewhat intrigued.

"Green woodpecker," announced Andrew. "Just look for

something about as big as a jackdaw but green with a yellow rump and it sort of undulates up and down as it flies."

"That's great," said Chris, "but let's keep walking or we'll be left behind." The rest of the party had descended into the woods, only to climb out of them on to a grass field above the river Rye.

For the next half mile or so silence descended on the group as a sort of pain barrier was passed. No one was used to walking great distances, no one had thought to exercise or get used to carrying a heavy pack, so an uncomfortable period of acclimatisation passed. The group soldiered on in silence, along the next path that descended silently through woodland and then emerged on to a small road.

"We go down the road, in fact we follow it for quite a while," said Robert, dutifully reading his map.

"In the book, it suggests we take a short detour and visit Rievaulx Abbey," added Andrew, flipping through the pages of the guidebook.

"Let's just wander up and look at Rievaulx Abbey," said Joe. "We've been doing Henry VIII in history – the dissolution of the monasteries and all that. The guidebook does say a bit about the place and the influence the monks had on the district. I reckon we should take the time for a look even though it's not officially part of the Cleveland Way."

"We should," added Chris, whose history teacher father had suggested just the same.

"Let's have a rest break when we get there then," Andreas suggested, leading the way up the road next to the river Rye.

"We're definitely having a break when we get there!" added a very fatigued Jeremy who was beginning to notice the discomfort from a blister forming on the back of his left heel. Thanks to football, Jeremy was one of the fitter members of the expedition. However, he was the only one in the group who smoked. Not regularly – just now and again in order to look cool – but who knows? Jeremy was short of breath and smoking probably wasn't helping.

At youth club, Joe had recently criticised Jeremy about his smoking, not through concern for his health, but through concern for the 'poofy' way he held his cigarettes. With his long flowing blond hair and slim, attractive features, Jeremy could appear quite feminine at times. Naturally, if you saw him on the football field, or listened to his comments on local females, you were left in no doubt that Jeremy was as straight as a die. But sometimes he did things that appeared, with no disrespect intended to the homosexual community, 'poofy'!

Joe's criticism of the way Jeremy held a cigarette was largely due to his stance and limp-wristed passing of cigarette from hand to lips.

"Don't do it, Jeremy," Joe had implored, as he stood outside the youth club one evening.

"Don't do what?" Jeremy asked.

"Don't smoke with your wrist so limp, you look like a puffta!"

At this, Jeremy pushed Joe to one side and then continued to smoke in a limp-wristed manner.

"Seriously, Jez, you're standing and dragging on that fag in a very female sorta way – pack it in, please?" Joe implored.

"Why should I? What's it to you anyway?!" said Jeremy, exhaling a series of rather cute smoke rings.

"I'll tell you why you oughta stop, Jez! You're turning me on, that's why!!" said Joe with one of his massive grins.

Joseph's words must have had some effect because, from that point on, Jeremy started holding his cigarettes in a more manly fashion!

Bringing up the rear of the group as they walked towards Rievaulx Abbey was Andrew, quite happy to be wandering alongside a river. Unbeknown to everyone else, he had finally seen the green woodpecker, but the sighting had been too fleeting to bring it to general attention. The next sighting, however, made him call everyone to a halt. "Hey, look at this then. This is a new one for me!"

Martin brought the group to a halt as his shared interest infected the rest, at least for a short time. "What you seen, Andy?"

"Over there on the rocks, look! Quick, just get me book out the side pocket."

"It's some sort of wagtail, isn't it?"

"Yes but is it a yellow or grey wagtail?"

"There's definitely yellow on it," observed Jeremy.

"It's a grey wagtail though," said Andrew. "It's grey on top, found near water and here, look," Andrew pointed at the book. "Here, borrow the binoculars and see for yourselves, it's a grey wagtail all right!"

"What's that then?" asked Martin as a larger, brownish bird with a white belly flew past rapidly, only a foot or so over the water.

"That was a dipper, a bloomin' dipper – wow, that's my first dipper!"

Meanwhile, over to the side of the road, Joe was looking uncomfortable. The sound of running water must have affected him.

"Wait a minute fellas, I've got to have a pee." With that, he hid himself behind a tree and relieved himself.

"If we don't keep moving, we're never going to get anywhere today," Robert added. "Come on, let's look at this Cistercian abbey, or at least the remains of it. I'm reading all this from the map by the way!"

"Don't worry, Rob, we didn't think you had suddenly become knowledgeable about something," Martin added. Robert began to chase his brother, but stopped when he realised Martin was heading the wrong way. The usual confrontation was prevented only by a desire to conserve energy.

The abbey at Rievaulx appeared enormous as it came into view in front of them. There was only one other person around and so the group could approach the ruins and even sit on some of the stone remains for their break without being challenged.

"Wow, it's massive!" said Joe, in admiring tones. "Fancy Henry VIII wrecking beautiful places like this. He wasn't the nicest of blokes, was he?"

"Well, he wasn't known for being very nice was he, just ask some of his wives!" Chris added.

"But just imagine how much work went into building this place, there were no machines back then were there, so how did they cut the blocks, carry them here and then build the place? It's fantastic!"

"Maybe they used slaves, you know forced to do it at the point of a sword," suggested Jeremy.

"They don't like it up 'em, Mr Mainwaring, they don't like it up 'em!" Andreas added, stealing lines from the TV show *Dad's Army*. Quoting from television programmes was definitely one of Andreas's trademarks. To be honest though, his rendition of 'Oh, Betty' from *Some Mothers Do 'Av 'Em* did irritate after a while.

Joe stared for a while before saying: "I don't reckon they were forced. They wanted to build it as a monument to their beliefs; they just didn't count on Henry VIII." Interestingly, Joe, being a protestant, was only too aware that Henry VIII's actions had laid the foundations of his own faith and the Reformation of the church so central to his beliefs. The majesty of the ruin and the beauty of the valley it stood in did cause Joe to have a brief religious moment. Without any embarrassment, he faced the abbey, bowed his head and mouthed a silent prayer.

As he walked away, Andreas quietly did an imitation of Frankie Howerd. "Titter ye not," he said, just loud enough for everyone, bar Joe, to hear. It was interesting to see that no one was the least inclined to 'titter'. Joe's religious reaction was in perfect harmony with the aura that this quiet and magnificent valley had projected into the atmosphere around the ruined abbey.

As they left the site, the whole group turned as one and stood silently looking at the ruin.

"It is magnificent even now, isn't it?" said Chris. "I mean, just imagine it with a roof and monks being called to prayer, maybe a bell ringing, or people singing or chanting."

Joseph was totally in awe of the ruined abbey. "They used to pray at all sorts of odd times, even in the middle of the night! Just imagine rows of monks chanting away walking under those arches holding flaming torches or candles on their way to the altar. It's just an amazing place, I'm really glad we detoured off the track to look at it! Having said that, though, we'd better get moving. Come on!"

Backpacks firmly in place again, the explorers marched back towards the ancient bridge over the Rye to regain contact with the Cleveland Way. High above the ridge to the east and above the remains of the old canal the monks had built to transport building materials, were dozens of rooks and jackdaws soaring and playing in the air.

As the road through Nettledale was so narrow, the walkers found themselves spreading out in single file. Robert was in the lead studying the map, closely followed by Joe and Jeremy.

Further back were Martin, Chris and Andreas. Bringing up the rear was Andrew, who was continually being delayed by trying to identify birds constantly calling or flying nearby. His latest sighting was of a sparrowhawk being mobbed high in the sky by a congregation of rooks and jackdaws.

Robert led the group off the road and through a gate leading to a small track making its way upwards through Nettledale. At this point, there was a mixing of positions and Andrew found himself second from the front. Just as well, as coming up on the right was a beautiful valley with a small stream meandering through it. Suddenly, a small brown bird with pale upper wing bars flew across the water calling plaintively. It landed on a small gravel outcrop and Andrew was immediately 'on to it' with his binoculars.

"Well, what is it?" asked Martin.

"I've no idea, it's a wader and I'm not so good at them. It's sat over there bobbing its tail up and down like a wagtail, but it's not a wagtail. I just don't know what it is. Here, have a look."

The binoculars were passed around while Andrew flicked through his bird book. When Andreas got the binoculars he took some time finding the bird, despite the fact it was being very cooperative and staying put, giving everyone a chance to see it. When he finally locked on to the bird, he made everyone laugh by imitating Bruce Forsyth on *The Generation Game* by saying: "Nice to see you, to see you nice!"

By the time everybody had sighted the new bird, Andrew had made his decision.

"Common sandpiper! It's a common sandpiper!! That's a first for me. It says here in the book 'often perches on low objects, bobbing its head and tail'. It's definitely doing that and the colour and the pale wing bars all fit."

"Why are you getting so excited over something that's common? I mean, if the book said 'incredibly rare sandpiper' I could see why you'd get excited, but common, no way!" Jeremy was testing the water, as it were, for a 'piss-take moment'. But the moment passed and everybody marched onward.

Robert was having difficulty picking out which of several tracks to take, but consensus was reached and the group found itself climbing out of the beautiful wooded valley of Flassendale to emerge on Low Field Lane leading to the village of Cold Kirby.

Immediately on leaving the woods, Jeremy looked around and said: "I thought we were supposed to be on the moors? I mean, this is farmland, there's no heather? We could have walked around the 'Vale'!"

"Ahh! But would we see dippers, grey wagtails and common sandpipers, Jeremy?" asked Andrew.

"Would I really want to? Would I be all that bothered, Andy?" chided a cynical Jeremy.

"Shut up, Jeremy!" Martin added. "Save your energy and keep walking."

"What about lunch? I'm starving. And I need a pee again, hang on." Joe stood up against a gate post and yet again added some nutrients to the North York Moors National Park.

"Waiting for him to pee is getting as bad as waiting for you to identify some flippin' bird." Chris commented to Andrew. "And look, he sets everyone else off!" Like some synchronous reflex action usually associated with yawning, the adventurers all found themselves looking for spots to relieve themselves.

Joe was soon back to food. "Well, when's lunch?"

"Dad said we should try and get to Sutton Bank for lunch 'cos the view's fantastic," replied Andrew, acutely aware that time was pressing on.

"Sutton Bank isn't that far now," added Robert after consulting his map. "Which explains those gliders, because the map says there's a gliding club right on the top. The track goes alongside the airfield," he pointed forwards and upwards to reveal two gliders soaring effortlessly across the sky in front of them.

"I've been in a glider," said Andreas, in a matter of fact tone. "It's part of being in the Air Training Corps. I've only been up once, but it was really good." Here then was confirmation that Andrew Price's mates led a more exciting life than he did! "It's just marvellous to be up there soaring around without any noise except the wind passing by."

"Hopefully, we won't experience similar feelings of the wind roaring past when we share your tent tonight, Andreas," added Andrew.

"It's not Andreas you should be worried about, Andrew," added Robert, with a knowing glance towards his twin brother. Rather worryingly for Joe, Martin simply smiled at his brother, as if this 'windy' characteristic was something to be proud of.

The Cleveland Way then passed through Cold Kirby and across more farmland, this time with the added interest of a lapwing doing a noisy display flight over a young cereal crop. A bit further on were beautiful racehorses being put through their paces on one of Britain's oldest racetracks at Hambleton House. The Cleveland Way then emerged at Hambleton Inn before following, for a short distance, the A170. A sign then directed the group on to a track through a pine forest with odd clumps of heather. The map indicated they were walking down Castern Dyke.

"There you go, Jeremy, heather. See, this is heather!" said Andrew, pointing out patches in among the pine trees.

"It's not what I thought of as moorland, though," commented a breathless Jeremy.

Any further discussion was stymied by the group's arrival at the edge of Sutton Bank. One by one, the walkers reached the edge, and one by one each was amazed by the contrast. From walking across open fields, deep wooded gullies and alongside babbling crystal clear rivers to this, the most fantastic view imaginable.

"What are the hills over there in the distance?" asked Joe.

Robert wasn't able to provide an answer from his map of the Cleveland Way, but Andrew had been told by his father what to expect. "Those hills are the Yorkshire Dales and the valley is the Vale of York, or at least it is at the bottom end. Further up it becomes the Vale of Mowbray. As we get to the Kilburn White Horse, we should be able to see York Minster to the south. Well, that's what Dad reckons."

Robert was studying the map. "So we've got to go south now as far as the White Horse, then we turn back and retrace our footsteps to here before carrying on north along the Cleveland Way. You know sooner or later we've got to find a campsite!"

"I reckon we're doing all right, we can keep going a while. Its two o'clock now, let's have half an hour for lunch then get on again," said Chris.

"Speak for yourself," said an anguished Andreas, who had discarded his backpack, taken off his boots and was massaging his sore feet.

"Anybody got blisters?" asked Chris.

"Thanks to wearing two pairs of socks, I reckon we're doin' well," commented Robert.

The only one with a blister was Jeremy, who had persisted with his vinegar treatment and hadn't put on two pairs of socks. It was, however, only a small blister and he certainly wasn't going to admit his vinegar treatment hadn't been completely successful.

Lunch was a simple affair of sandwiches, which everyone had brought from home together with a slice of fruit cake supplied by Andrew's mum. They all carried their own stash of chocolate and silence reigned as Marathon and Mars bars were consumed.

Lunch over, the serious business of getting packs back on began. Naturally, there was the usual wait for Joe to urinate, made all the more remarkable as he had gone just before eating. But soon they were off again along the rim of Roulston Scar, with the mowed grass of the glider station on the left. The quiet was broken by the sound of a loud motor and across the grass swept a graceful glider. It was being towed by a long cable, which in turn was being winched towards a stationary machine at the other end of the glider strip. The glider ascended steeply before releasing the cable after it had achieved some consider-able altitude.

"That's what we did at Spitalgate airfield," said Andreas, much to the admiration of his colleagues.

"Were you on your own?" asked Chris.

"No, you've got to get your 'wings' for that, we all had a turn with an instructor. It was a two-seater and it was great fun – we even did a loop the loop! That's why I want to join the air force!"

"Crikey, look at this cliff," said Martin as he approached the edge of Roulston Scar, "and look at the view – it's fantastic. What a place!"

"It's the cliff that's keeping the gliders up there today. The wind hits the hills and deflects vertically, all the gliders have to do is ride the air as it passes upward. Dead easy. In the summer there's thermals to ride as well. Hot air rises off rocky places and the pilots spot it and ride up on the air." Andreas was in his element and he had an appreciative audience.

Jeremy brought him down to earth by adding: "I suppose you have to be careful, Zorba, that the change in air pressure doesn't bust all your spots! You'd make a right mess of the cockpit!"

"That's really nice, Jeremy. Really, really nice. With friends like you who needs enemies," said Martin, rallying to Andreas's defence.

Even his brother turned on Jeremy, singing part of Alvin Stardust's 'Jealous Mind'.

Jeremy quickly apologised: "Sorry, 'Dreas," and the air was cleared.

Just to the side of the track appeared the White Horse. Not that it was recognisable as a horse from this angle. It certainly didn't look as obvious as it did from miles away on their arrival in the Vale of York that morning. The land fell steeply away from the side of the track so all that could be seen was the top part of the head and the eye.

"Let's all get on the eye for a photo," said Chris, who had been given a Kodak Instamatic for Christmas.

"We can't do that, we just can't," said Andrew.

"Why the hell not?" asked an incredulous Chris. "Don't tell me there's a rare bird nesting on there!"

"It says here in the guidebook that 'you are asked not to walk on the horse.' They're restoring it and I guess all the footprints don't do it any good!" The do-gooder bit of Andrew's personality was being displayed.

In the end, a photo was taken of the entire group standing on the eye, minus Andrew who declined to walk on the horse. The camera had to be set on the self-timer and placed on a post next to the site. This was because Andrew refused to be party to 'environmental vandalism' of such magnitude and wouldn't even take the picture!

"Sometimes, Price, you can be a total prick," said Jeremy. It was generally agreed that Andrew needed to lighten up, but nobody really expected any change, so the incident was forgotten – well at least this time!

"Well, we've seen it like the guidebook said we should, so we'd better turn around and keep going," said Andrew, acutely aware that his environmental stance on the White Horse was going to need some remedial work to heal the wounds. "But before we go, perhaps you would like to borrow my binoculars and look over there," and he pointed away off to the south of the White Horse. "I reckon that building over there is York Minster, what do you all think?"

One by one, the binoculars were passed round and York Minster recognised. Beyond the great monument in York could be seen several power station cooling towers, but no one was sure how far they were looking. Joe focused the group's attention once again on more menial concerns.

"I've no idea where we're going to camp, but I tell you what, I'll be glad when we get there. I'm knackered," said Joe, who was constantly leaning from one side to another in order to spread the pain that his low hung rucksack was beginning to cause. This met with general agreement from everyone and it seemed to spur the walkers on. In no time they had crossed the A170 again and were heading along the edge of Sutton Brow, White Mare Crag and Whitestone Cliff.

Gormire Lake, set among bare deciduous forest, sat like a jewel beneath them. Joe was especially taken with the view of the lake.

"Don't we get to walk around it then? I love walking near water," he asked.

"I reckon you spend a lot of time walking near water anyway, Joe. I mean the number of times you go for a pee it must be like walking along a towpath most of the time," Jeremy added.

"Thanks a lot, Jezz, I've got a weak bladder, that's all, or very efficient kidneys," Joe was a little annoyed. "Actually, my surname has got something to do with being next to a river or water course. It's of German origin, or from somewhere else in Europe."

"Weak bladder's got nothing to do with it, Joe! You just like flashing your whatsit around, don't you mate?" joked Martin. "I mean, that's why the anagram of your name is Penis J K Horn!"

A wave of laughter barely distracted from what was now becoming painful walking for everybody.

"Hey, Robert, what does the map say? Is there a farm or anything coming up to camp on? I don't reckon it'll be long before it starts getting dark," asked Chris, starting to get concerned.

"There is one there, look, called Southwoods Farm but it's a long way down. Up here though, the track gets really close to this place." Robert's finger landed on a farm just down the hill from the track near Sneck Yate Bank. The general feeling was to try and get to this farm before dark.

Despite aching feet, haversacks cutting into shoulder blades and ever increasing hunger pangs, the group marched on. It didn't look so far on the map, but in reality this proved to be the hardest part of the day. Despite this, everyone still had the energy to appreciate the rugged grandeur of Boltby Scar, the disused quarry and the view over Boltby and beyond.

At dusk, a tired group of seven walkers descended down the ridge towards a farm. All seven approached the imposing farmhouse, but it was left to Robert and Andrew to address the farmer. After explaining what they were doing and adding that they would leave no litter, or indeed any sign they had ever been there, the kindly landowner agreed to let them camp on a level field a good half mile from the yard. The farmer showed them a dustbin into which they could place rubbish in the morning and an outside tap from which drinking water could be obtained.

A bedraggled group made their way to the camping spot and began, in failing light, to erect their tents. Setting up camp proved to be a relatively fast and efficient process spurred on by everyone's desire for a good night's sleep. After tents were erected and sleeping bags unfurled came the preparation for their first main meal. This consisted of tinned stewed steak with rehydrated mashed potatoes and bread. The whole process proved to be a slick and well-coordinated effort. Everyone pulled their weight and got right into the tasks that needed to be done.

After the meal and some rudimentary washing up by torch light, they all slipped into their sleeping bags only to realise that the floor was hard – very hard. Not only that, it was cold, so cold that all their spare clothes had to be worn to give their walking clothes a chance to air.

Andreas had the last words as he called out, in fair imitation of Hodges from the *Dad's Army* TV programme: "Put that light out!"

He got a resounding and well synchronised chorus of "shut up, Zorba" for his trouble.

Chapter 7

Sneck Yate Bank to Osmotherley

The seven adventurers slept soundly until two o'clock in the morning. Chris woke up to find the tent he was sharing with Andrew and Andreas was experiencing problems.

"What's the smell? Oh my god, it stinks in here!"

Andrew woke with enough time to hear and understand Chris's remark.

"Oh, Christ Almighty, is there a dead chicken in here or something!" Andrew shouted, in alarm.

Meanwhile the third occupant, Andreas, could be heard laughing.

From the next tent came the voice of religious reason as Joe responded to Andrew's comment.

"Hey, you lot! Don't take the Lord's name in vain, please!"

An anguished Andrew asked: "Is 'what's that terrible, sodding smell,' more reasonable and polite then Joseph?"

"That's much better, thanks, Andy mate!"

Meanwhile, Andreas was still chuckling to himself as he lay between Andrew and Chris in the three-man tent.

"For goodness sake, what is the stink?" asked Andrew again. "And what are you laughing at Andre... Oh no, it's not you is it? You haven't farted have you? Please tell us it's not true!"

Andreas replied between paroxysms of laughter: "Sorry fellas, I'm really sorry!"

Chris rolled his head towards the wall and through clenched teeth said: "Well don't flap your sleeping bag, hold it tight round your neck, ya smelly prick. No! It's too bad!" The sound of the zip on Chris's side of the tent could be heard. For some reason at night, in the quiet, this unzipping sounded incredibly loud. This was followed by the sound of Chris thrusting his head out of the tent and thudding it on to the wet grass beyond. Deep breathing of sweet, fresh air followed.

From within the tent came a stupendous breaking of wind followed by yet another apology, punctuated by laughter from Andreas. This was instantly followed by Andrew ejecting his head from the tent. Andrew's laboured breathing joined Chris's outside the tent.

"What the hell's wrong with you, Zorba?" asked Andrew.

"I reckon I'm allergic to stewed tin beef!"

"Tonight's beef stew you mean?" asked Chris.

"Yeah, it was really nice wasn't it? I really enjoyed that meal."

Andrew was quick to reply. "Well I hope you made the most of it, 'cos it's the last time you're havin' it!"

Amid peals of laughter, Andreas added: "We've still got four cans left!"

From Joe's tent came the voice of Martin. "Will you lot shut up, we're trying to sleep!"

From the same tent there came the sound of the tent flap being unzipped and the voice of Joseph. "Now I'm awake I've got to go to the loo. Pass the trowel, Mart."

"You're not serious! A number two? At this time of night?"

"No, I just thought I ought to bury my pee."

"What the hell for! You haven't been burying them have you! If you had been we'd still be back at Sutton Bank. Jesus Joe, just go out and have a pee and make sure you get well away from the tent!"

"All right, all right but just cut out taking the Lord's name in vain!"

There followed all the sounds associated with a tired, stiff, cold and yet very religious young man urinating on a cold clear night: religious, because during the entire interlude Joe decided to sing the hymn 'For Those in Peril on the Sea', except he changed 'on the sea' to 'having a pee'.

"Can you hear that?" Chris asked. "That singing is going on and on and so is his urine flow. I don't know about him turning water into wine, but I reckon he'd beat Jesus turning water into urine!"

"Hey, Joe! Go steady out there or you'll flood the entire Vale of York!" Andrew yelled across at him.

Until now the tent occupied by Jeremy and Robert had been silent. Suddenly the voice of Jeremy could be heard above Joe's tuneful rendition of 'For Those in Peril Having a Pee'.

"Oh God no, you've got to be joking!"

Laughing, both Andrew and Chris responded: "What's up, Jeremy?" "Yeah, what's up Jez?"

"It stinks in here as well. Oh, crikey, let me out!" The tent zip could be heard as well as laughter from all those listening.

Through more laughter Robert's voice could now be heard. "Well, maybe I'm allergic to beef stew as well?"

At this point, Joe, still happily watering Yorkshire, produced what is generally termed a 'rip-snorter'. A fart loud enough to make the golden retriever way over in the farm yard bark in response. At this irreverence the entire group burst into laughter. Then Joe could be heard walking through the grass back to his tent. The main zip was opened and Joe asked Martin for the trowel – yet again.

"Hey Mart, pass the trowel mate please and the roll of toilet paper!"

"What, you're kidding, I mean we've already had this conversation!"

"I know, but you see I followed through with that one. It's a pity, 'cos I've only got one spare pair of undies!"

Martin could be heard rummaging amongst the rucksacks muttering: "Did you have to tell me that, Joe? I just didn't need to know any part of what you just said!"

Amid general laughter, Andrew sounded the environmental warning. "Walk well away from the tent, Joe, and dig it deep. We don't want anything visible for the farmer."

Joseph's voice could be heard mumbling as he wandered away: "Yeah, yeah, I'm going, I'm going!"

"How far has he gone? I mean look, the torch light is miles away. I reckon he's going to Sutton Bank!" Chris observed before continuing: "You know what; I'm sleeping the rest of the night with my head out of the tent. It's safer."

"So am I," Andrew replied. "How you going, Jeremy?"

Jeremy's voice could be heard, just as Joe returned from his digging and re-entered his tent. "Shut up everybody, and chuck out them beef stew cans!"

Then everyone drifted off to sleep once again.

Jeremy was first awake in the morning. Not because he was a light sleeper or any keener to get up than the rest of the group, but because the farm dog decided to lick his face. Not just a tentative and reluctant tongue exploration, but a passionate French kiss, the likes of which Jeremy had so far only dreamed of getting from the girls he knew at school The experience was diminished considerably when Jeremy realised that the second tongue in his mouth belonged to a dog!

"Oh shit, oh shit a brick, you've gotta be kidding! Go away, go on right away. That's it, sod off! Toothpaste quick. Outta the way! Move it Rob, move!"

It was ten minutes to seven. Everyone was laughing: a good start to the day.

Daylight was breaking and the birds were beginning to sing. An inversion layer placed a glacier of fog below the campsite and the effect was breathtakingly beautiful. Admittedly, though, it was exceptionally cold. One by one the seven young men emerged from their tents rubbing hands together to generate heat.

Andreas was first out and soon had one of the gas stoves heating water. Each member of the team struggled to get blood circulating through tired and cold limbs, the pain of which was counter-balanced by the spectacular view across the valley. The presence of the cloud filling the valley beneath the moors gave the scene a dream-like quality. It felt like the campsite was not only remote, but in another world. The air was still and cold, but the sunshine was bright and warming. The grass was covered in moisture and tiny droplets stuck to a myriad of spiders' webs strewn amongst the long grass in the paddock. The only sound came from a couple of jackdaws, bleating lambs and a distant tractor.

The initial conversation centred on the ignominious way Jeremy had been woken! Naturally the farm retriever had gained celebrity status and it received a fair bit of attention from the hikers.

"There you go, Jez, you always wanted to know what snogging was really like," said Martin as he stroked the dog's head while standing behind it. Unfortunately for Martin, his joke severely backfired. Not visible to him, as he stroked the dog's head, the animal had become aroused. This resulted in much amusement from those who could see what was going on.

"I think that dog really likes you, Martin!" said his brother, Robert.

"Maybe you should give it a bone, Mart?" suggested Jeremy, tongue in cheek.

The comic scenario broke down when Chris laid it on the line by adding: "Yeah, Mart, give it a bone before it gives you one!" At this point, Martin realised what was going on and sheepishly left the dog alone.

Breakfast was next on the list. The water boiling on the gas stove was used to make tea. Milk powder was added to cold water for corn flakes and Rice Krispies. Eggs were fried and eaten with slices of bread. One or two of the group disappeared into nearby trees with the trowel and, meanwhile, pots and pans were cleaned as best they could be in the diminishing supply of water. Solid streaks of egg white remained on many of the frying pans for the duration of the walk as they always proved difficult to clean off with cold water and a J-cloth. Finally, tents were dismantled and rucksacks packed. All that remained was for Andrew to do his last-minute inspection of the site for rubbish.

Finally, everyone headed to the farmyard to refill water bottles at the outside tap the farmer had kindly indicated the night before. The only person none too happy was Joe, who had misplaced one of his sponges and was desperately searching the pockets of his rucksack for the missing item.

The farmer was up and about and wandered over to the group.

"Well lads, did thee 'av a good neight? Ah could 'ear y'all laffin' at two in t'morning! You've bin 'avin' fun then, ay?"

"Yes, well, you could say that, we did have some disturbance at around two o'clock," said Robert.

"You see the wind got up and woke us all for a while!" added Andreas, with something of a twinkle in his eye.

"Well it were t'dog as woke me up like! Ah could 'ear thee

all laffin' an' chattin'. Then I caught glimpse of torch light over in yon woods; follard by laffin' so ah knew ye was alreet! Sounds like yer 'avin' an adventure lads! So t'wind got up a bit, eh! Talkin' of weather young 'uns, forecasts for a warm 'un today so I'd put thee coats on 'cos they allus gets it wrong!"

"What do you farm?" enquired Andrew.

"Well, lad, we 'as a small suckler 'erd o' shorthorns down 'ere in t'lower meadows; a lot o' ewes lambin' up round 'ere, they'll be up on't moors soon enough an' we've some spring barley farther down t'vale like. Any of you lads in farmin' then?"

"I'm on a chicken farm! Not as pretty as this place, though. All our birds are indoors in cages, so the work is dusty and a bit grotty at times," said Andrew.

"We keep pigs!" added Andreas. "And, like him, the work at our place is a bit grotty. Not out in the great outdoors like here."

"I reckon keeping chickens in cages is cruel, Andrew," said a concerned Jeremy. "When you showed us in your sheds I thought it was pretty sick. I mean, look at this place with sheep and cattle running free. It's a massive difference!"

The Yorkshire farmer gave a measured response, almost leaping to the defence of intensive agriculture. "Aye, there's a lot o' people to feed out there an' me'be pigs an' poultry kept intensive is the only way forrard. Rum 'un, int it? Tell ee summat though, these sheep an' cattle looks none too 'appy when it's chuckin' it down wi' rain and they has to stay outside like! Any road, lads, so long as thee's cleaned up thee mess where yon tents were an' as long as thee shuts gates after thee sens, then it's bin a pleasure 'avin ye stay! Good luck on't rest o' t'walk. Cheerio young 'uns!"

With a smile, sincere thank yous and a parting wave, the

seven began the climb up Sneck Yate Bank to rejoin the Cleveland Way.

The initial walking proved very hard as stiff and tired muscles had to be persuaded to perform again. Jeremy's small blister felt better protected as he now wore two pairs of socks. Robert was leading and holding the map as he searched for the start of the track. This soon presented itself in the form of a forestry gate, next to which a Cleveland Way sign gave direction.

"This looks nice, we might see some new birds in here," said the ever optimistic Andrew. "In fact, there you go already! Listen, can you hear that?"

"What is it?" asked Chris.

"You mean what are they? Over there, that's a chiffchaff calling. It's very early really 'cos that's a migrant. Only just got here from Africa. That loud call over there is a great tit. Listen! That soft little call up in the larch trees, that's a goldcrest, one of England's smallest birds. Brilliant, I've only heard them once before and that was in conifer trees at Eyebrook Reservoir."

But the group was spreading out again and so birdwatching was curtailed allowing everyone to catch up. Joe was in the most pain as the straps on his rucksack began to cut into his shoulders.

"Which one of you bastards has nicked one of me sponges? Come on, it's not funny. These straps are killing me."

Andreas reassured him: "None of us have got your sponges, Joe, honest. They weren't lying round the campsite were they, so they must be wrapped up in your sleeping bag or in your tent. Here, have an Opal Fruit." Andreas passed around a packet of chewy sweets which, while tasting very nice, did leave everyone short of breath. Cleverly though, it did stop Joe complaining about something nobody could do anything about.

The track angled upwards through a forestry plantation to go on right past High Paradise Farm. After a sharp left hand turn the track ran on to the old drovers road known as Hambleton Road. The Cleveland Way then followed this track through the upper part of Boltby Forest with tantalising views of open moorland to the east. Finally, the group emerged on to the moors with light grassland in the foreground and extensive areas of heather surrounding it. For the seven young men from Leicestershire, such moorland vista was a new experience.

"Now, that's more like what I was expecting when you said moorland," said an awe-struck Jeremy.

"It's more or less moorland I suppose. I mean the more I think of it, it's moorland. You want any more?" asked Joe, playing with the English language again.

"All right, Joe. I mean you can't help being a moor-on can you?" Jeremy replied appropriately.

Martin was doing some birdwatching. "Hey, Andrew, what are they?" he enquired, pointing to two large brown birds with long curved beaks flying up over the moors.

The birds answered the question themselves by uttering their familiar and distinctive mournful trill.

Martin quickly said, "You don't need to tell me, they're curlews." Just for once the entire group were transfixed as they listened to this quintessential moorland bird call.

Chris broke the spell. "Come on, let's get moving. Let's get a few more miles under our belts before we have some lunch." Which is exactly what they did, once they had waited for Joe to complete yet another toilet break!

The day was beautifully clear but with a cold wind blowing from the west. Lunch was eaten in the shelter of the stone wall that runs right alongside the Cleveland Way on this section of the moors. Unlike the day before, there was plenty of time for a leisurely meal break as tonight's camp was to be in the village of Osmotherley, which, according to the map, was not all that far away.

Rucksacks were leaned against the wall and sandwiches prepared followed by chocolate bars and biscuits. All very civilised and, thanks to the weather, very easily achieved.

"Where are we camping tonight then?" asked Chris. Andrew began consulting the guidebook, but Robert provided the answer.

"On the map there's a campsite marked just north of the village. We should have plenty of time to get there."

"We may well have time, but will we have the energy?" enquired Jeremy, who like everyone was feeling fatigued from yesterday's exertions.

At this point, a solitary male walker travelling from the opposite direction approached them. The hiker wore a long brown overcoat that hung down below his knees. He wore a cowboy-style hat, carried a small canvas knapsack and in his left hand he held a stout, but gnarled, stick.

"Gudday, fellas," he cheerily announced. "And what are yous all doing then? Crikey you've got enough gear, or is it all tucker in them rucksacks!"

"We're doing what you're doing, but going the other way round," replied Andreas.

"Are you Australian?" asked Martin.

"Struth, is me accent that strong, cobber! Yep I'm a true blue, fair dinkum Aussie mate. Just back in the Mother Country checking on me roots and by that I don't mean looking up old girlfriends, if yous get me drift!"

None of the group did get his drift, but it was nice to talk to someone new.

"Have you walked all the way from Filey?" Jeremy asked.

"No way, mate, I'm not on walkabout! You'd have to be mad to do that! No, I'm just doing from Osmotherley to Sutton Bank then I'm back with the relis to York. Tell you what though, it's a lovely spot, best bit of England I've seen. No wonder me dad always called Yorkshire God's own county. Hey! You lads doing the whole walk down the coast are you?" A chorus of yeses prompted him to answer. "Bloody oath! Well bloody good luck to you all. I takes me hat off to ya. Well done and bloody good luck!" With that the Antipodean gentleman did indeed tip his Akubra and strode off towards the south whistling 'Along the Road to Gundagai' as he went.

"See," said Jeremy, "it is unusual to walk the whole flamin' lot carrying all this cobber, I mean clobber! See, he thinks we're mad! We are mad. We should never have said yes. Bloody Price and his crazy ideas!"

"Just take it easy, Jez," said Joe. "We're just tired. Remember how impressed he sounded that we were doing the entire walk? I mean, come on fellas, this is quite a thing we're all doing, so let's keep our spirits up." After the pep talk Joe leapt the wall to enable him to urinate on the other side with some semblance of privacy.

After a pleasant lunch and half an hour's sleep it was time to move on. The well-rehearsed routine of lifting rucksacks on to tired shoulders was executed and the group marched ever onward. The track stretched out alongside Black Hambleton with lovely farmland views to the west across the moors. After walking alongside a forested area for some time the track began to descend. This brought howls of protest from all the walkers as descending with tired legs and heavy packs was harder than climbing. The pain was, however, made bearable by fantastic moorland views with Osmotherley Moor and the Cleveland Hills away in the distant north.

When the Cleveland Way met up with the Osmotherley to Hawnby Road, Robert began checking the map.

"We go off this way down Oakdale. Looks like you're going to get your wish to walk by water, Joe, 'cos we walk past a couple of reservoirs on the way down to Osmotherley. Not far now!"

At this stage the group entered a silent phase. Everybody was concentrating on putting one tired and painful foot after the next. The reservoirs created some interest, but there were no water birds worthy of ornithological excitement and even if there had been, Andrew Price would have been pushed to notice because even he was concentrating solely on putting one foot in front of another. Gradually, the seven walkers became separated by up to 30 yards.

Robert was first to approach Osmotherley via a series of small lanes, tiny paddocks and little gateways. Standing next to a narrow alleyway at the end of a paddock, on the very edge of Osmotherley, was a man in dungarees and heavy boots.

"Hello," said Robert. "Are we nearly in Osmotherley?"

Unfortunately, this particular gentleman was 'intellectually challenged'. He didn't give the appearance of being retarded in any way at all until he answered. Then an unintelligible, loud and alarming series of noises erupted from his mouth and at the same time he wildly gesticulated in a most unnerving manner. Maybe this was some prank, or maybe the poor man was genuinely mentally retarded. Either way, the seven walkers should have been more perceptive and so more sympathetic to his problems. However, the fact remains that each and every one of the seven made separate overtures to this gentleman as they entered Osmotherley and each and every one was taken aback by the exact same response.

Robert hesitated as he reached Osmotherley and waited for

the next arrival.

"Did you just say anything to that chap?" he asked Jeremy, who was next into town.

"Did I what? That scared the life out of me. Why didn't you warn me!"

The sound of someone running with their rucksack bouncing came next. "Bloody hell, did you talk to that fella? That was really weird!!" Martin added as he arrived truly shaken.

One by one, the experience happened to everyone and one by one it entered everyone's memory of Osmotherley. Naturally, Joe was deeply sympathetic to the individual concerned and very critical of those who derived amusement from the incident.

"He couldn't help it, could he; I mean it wasn't like he did any harm, just his way of welcoming us all. Come on you lot, you've got to be more tolerant and you don't take the piss out of those less fortunate than yourself. We had to write some poetry in English and, you know what, I reckon mine is appropriate for this very moment!

On the cliff of sanity, upon the edge we stay,
To fall is certain madness, to stop is to delay.
The cliff is oh so sturdy, as people gather 'round.
One slip, one push, one falter, and you go tumbling down.
So if you see a madman, don't laugh at him or call,
One step alone divides you, one push, one sudden fall."

For his profound words Joseph received a round of applause, appreciative nodding of heads and several slaps on the back!

Andreas was thinking of food and comfort. "Let's buy some food in the village, there's got to be a shop somewhere. Then we can get to the campsite, set up early and sort out a bit and plan the next stage. What do you reckon?"

"That's a brilliant idea, especially if it includes lying down and resting my legs," said a tired and pain-wracked Jeremy.

The seven hikers found themselves on the main street in Osmotherley with a selection of small shops and a couple of public houses to choose from. A small bakery-cum-general store was selected and various meat pies, chipped potatoes and items of confectionery purchased.

On the way out of the shop, Andreas started laughing uncontrollably. A polite distance from the building, Chris asked the obvious question.

"Well come on then, 'Dreas, share the joke. What's tickled you so flamin' much?"

"Didn't you see the sign in the window? Look back there, it says Master Bakers of Repute. I mean 'master bakers'!"

Everyone looked 'gone out' at Andreas as he creased himself laughing at the innuendo he thought so amusing.

Andrew replied for everybody. "We know what you reckon is funny, 'Dreas, but believe me it's not that amusing, unless in Greek it's something else altogether! What really bothers me though is how you will undoubtedly work it into a chat-up line next time you're dancing with some buxom young lady in Nottingham? I can just hear it coming. You'll walk over and start dancing with some classy looking bird, the music will stop and as usual you won't have planned your opening line. You'll look lovingly into her eyes, lean over and yell: 'Hi baby! In my spare time, I'm a masturbator of some repute!'"

This did get a round of laughter, mainly because Andreas definitely had a reputation for saying odd things at very inappropriate times.

Chris and Jeremy had managed to flick through a newspaper while in the shop. They were both looking for the football score from Monday night's game. Chris was disappointed to read that Sheffield United had beaten Liverpool one-nil.

"Looks more and more like Leeds will end up top of the First Division," he reluctantly admitted to Jeremy.

The foodstuffs were carried out of the shop to be consumed in the centre of Osmotherley, where a wooden seat and stone steps provided some comfort.

Joe found a phone box and tried his luck at phoning Yvonne, but she wasn't in so he returned to the group with a worried look.

"Her mum said she wasn't in! Where would she be at this time of the afternoon? She couldn't even tell me what time she was going to be back! After we get our tents set up can we come back in the village? I want to try phoning again."

Robert decided it was time to impart some of his knowledge and experience. "I wouldn't bother, Joe. Don't phone again, it makes you look needy."

"I am needy! I can honestly say I'm in need of something, Robert! Especially from Yvonne!"

"Well my advice to you, Joe, is not to phone back. Be a giver of grief, not a taker!"

"Well you certainly provided me with some grief in that tent of ours last night, Rob!" Jeremy added.

"I reckon we're all in for some grief," said Chris pointing to the sky. "So far we've been lucky – no rain – but look at them clouds. They look a bit black to me. I reckon we're in for some rain later."

"Come on, fellas, let's get to the campsite," said Joe, easing himself upright from the grassy bank he was sitting on.

There followed a chorus of groans and moans as reluctant muscles were coaxed back into motion.

"How far is this campsite, Rob?" asked Martin. "I never

thought standing up would ever be this difficult! It nearly doesn't pay to stop, 'cos starting up again is agony!"

"This way, up the hill," said Robert, leading the way out of the centre of Osmotherley.

"Just had to be uphill didn't it? Couldn't be level or anything, could it?" moaned Jeremy, and this time his complaints were thought and shared by everyone else as well.

The campsite route continued upwards through Osmotherley and past the sign indicating tomorrow's onward track. The road then descended down into a wooded valley with the sound of running water at the bottom. The campsite was new. The owners relieved the seven hikers of 87.5 pence each and showed them a flat grassy area on which to erect their tents. A couple of levels above the campsite was a brand-spanking-new toilet and ablution block. For the seven adventurers it was paradise!

"First things first, let's get the tents up. Then we can clean up and maybe go back into Osmotherley later on. What do you reckon?" asked Chris.

"Sounds like a good idea to me, and you know what, walking without that rucksack on is going to feel really good," said Jeremy.

Setting up the tents, rolling out sleeping bags and stashing rucksacks and possessions was conducted with practised precision. For Joe, the process was particularly rewarding because, as his sleeping bag unfurled, out fell his precious sponge. Tomorrow's walking was going to be so much easier.

Andrew and Robert made time to discuss the next day's walk. As they followed the Cleveland Way on the map they began to realise that the next stretch was not exactly easy. Apart from several big undulations, downhill and up dale, the route didn't appear to go near any towns or villages.

"Where the heck will we camp tomorrow? I mean, I don't want to walk far from the track, but there are no campsites or anything for miles unless we descend to the villages on the lowlands like Carlton, Busby or Great Broughton," commented Andrew.

"You're right. Unless we walk miles extra we're just going to have to find a farm again like last night's! Hey fellas, make the most of the facilities on this site, 'cos tomorrow we're camping on the moors or on a farm somewhere!" announced Robert to anyone listening.

The next hour was taken up with restoring cleanliness. For the first time in their lives, a toilet was truly appreciated. The alternative – Joe's shovel – was definitely not the preferred choice. Best of all was the hot shower, which seemed to ease aching muscles and restore a sense of equilibrium.

The only thing that proved disturbing was the sight of Andreas squeezing spots in front of a bright new mirror above the hand basins. Those members of the expedition who witnessed the squiggly yellow marks appearing on the mirror in front of him will never be the same again! Osmotherley, for Andrew, Robert and Jeremy, will for ever be synonymous with the colour yellow and visions of Andreas contorting himself to reach hard to get at 'fissure vents' on the side of the main volcano – namely, his face.

There was just time, after setting up camp and cleaning up, to return to Osmotherley before the little shop selling food closed. Another serving of chips and hot meat pies meant that cooking was definitely not necessary. Joe made a return visit to the public phone box after cadging a ten pence coin from Martin and, yet again, he found himself speaking to Yvonne's mother, who was pleasant, but a trifle brusque. After the call, he returned disconsolately to the group.

"Well that was quick! She's either chucked ya, or she's still out – either way you've just shown weakness by phoning her up. She wins, you lose!" said a sarcastic and unsympathetic Robert.

"She's still out and her mum doesn't know where she is. Come to think of it, that's really wrong, 'cos her mum always knows where she is and when I asked when she's back she said she didn't know. That's really wrong, 'cos she likes to know when she's due back and there was no message for me! Now that's really wrong, 'cos she always leaves me a message if she can't get to the phone. This is wrong, so wrong!! She's with somebody else, I just know it!" Joe sat on the wooden seat near the phone box with his elbows on his knees and his head in his hands. He was the epitome of misery!

A whispered conversation between Jeremy, Robert and Martin saw the three band members erupt into song with Don Mclean's 'American Pie':

"He was singin' bye-bye, Miss American Pie.
Drove my Chevy to the levee but the levee was dry.
Them good old boys were drinkin' whiskey and rye
and singin' 'this'll be the day that I die,
this'll be the day that I die'"

"Why you singin' that? It's nothing to do with a love going wrong! It's all about the plane crash that killed Buddy Holly, Ritchie Valens and the Big Bopper. The day the music dies is Don McLean lamenting the end of his version of rock and roll. Honestly, fellas!" an incredulous Joe replied.

"What about when he gets into 'now I know that you're in love with him 'cos I saw you dancing in the gym; you both kicked off your sho-oe's; man, I dig them rhythm and blues," added Jeremy, very tunefully.

"Well that bit's appropriate, but the rest is just lamenting the end of a musical era. Even the bit about the levee being dry is metaphorically referring to the music fading away," added Joe, yet again showing his superior knowledge of the music of the age.

"I should have known something was wrong. Before I came on this walk she sat me down and played Ralph McTell's *Spiral Staircase* album. There's this song called 'Streets of London' that ends with the words 'I'll show you something to make you change your mind.' She was trying to tell me not to go on the walk! Oh God, I'm going to have to go home!"

Martin sat next to Joseph, put his arm around him and genuinely expressed his sympathy.

"Joe, you're not going home just for her. This walk is only for ten days and if she won't let you do something like this at this time of your life what's she goin' to do in the future? I thought you wanted to go to university? You'll be away for longer than ten days if you go there. You're the one who pointed out the significance of this walk as being like the last bit of true freedom we're all going to get! No Joe, if you pack in, we all pack in. Isn't that right fellas?"

A chorus of 'yep', 'too right' and 'too true' greeted Martin's comment, and Joe seemed to respond positively. Despite all the usual banter and leg pulling that occurred every day when the group were together, tonight's group reaction left Joe in no doubt that he was among friends who genuinely felt his pain. This was despite the fact Robert started singing 'All You Need Is Love' as they walked back to the campsite! Andreas quietly made the comment that he was sure he had heard Joe take the Lord's name in vain, but he was ignored as well.

On return to the tents, nobody needed persuading to go to

bed early and by 8.30pm all seven were fast asleep. Had they been awake they would have noticed an ominous change in temperature and visibility, as moist clouds descended and a cold breeze began to develop. Wednesday's walking was going to put the entire group to the test. Frankly, the best thing they could have done that night was sleep.

Chapter 8

Osmotherley to Hasty Bank

The first thing everybody noticed as they woke on Wednesday morning was a distinct drop in temperature and the sound of tents creaking in a stiff breeze. The next thing of note emerged as heads were stuck out of the tents. The moving air was white and moist and visibility, even in the confines of the campsite, was very much reduced. From the tents the ablution block, clearly visible the previous night before it got dark, could not now be seen. Furthermore, even though it wasn't raining as such, just an exploratory exposure of the face to the elements resulted in water forming rivulets down the cheeks, which then dripped from the chin.

One by one, the hikers emerged from their tents and ran to the toilet block. Breakfast became cereal served inside the tents with bread and jam and hot tea brewed by Andreas and Chris under the porch of the toilet block. From the word go, every member of the party donned wet-weather clothing. During the packing up of sleeping bags and spare clothing, any dry items were placed in plastic bags. Finally, the tents were dismantled quickly and packed away after fly sheets were shaken to remove surface drips. The whole exercise was approached with military precision and speed. The value of last night's clean up and early night was not underestimated by anyone.

Then, with rucksacks packed and wet-weather gear donned, the expedition set off up the hill towards Osmotherley. At the top of the rise, Robert led the way on to the next section of the walk by turning on to a narrow, stony track, heading west across the hillside. With hoods pulled up over ears, the group was strangely silent as conversation proved difficult. The wind tended to disperse voices to such an extent that the only way to be understood was to turn around and address directly the face behind. Generally, it proved far easier to say nothing and just soldier on.

As the track rounded the hill to head north again it passed into a field.

"You sure we're on the right track, Rob?" asked Martin.

"So far, so good, Martin. We should find a wood after this field and head up to the top of the hill above Mount Grace Priory. That's if we're right, of course!" replied Robert. His tone was civil, revealing that today he was taking things very seriously, as he was only too aware that in the mist his map reading skills were very necessary to the success of the day's hike.

"Hey, can we get a look at Mount Grace Priory?" asked Joe, who had enjoyed reading the history of Yorkshire's only Carthusian house. "It was built in about 1400 and the monks used to live their lives secluded in little cells. Apparently, you can still make out the little rooms they used to be in."

"Sorry, Joe, we haven't got time today. It's wet and we've miles to go. We really will have to keep going, we've enough on our plates just getting through the walk today," said Robert who, thanks to the weather, was the only one to hear Joe's plea.

Joe didn't give in so easily and turned to Jeremy.

"Hey, Jez, you wanna see Mount Grace Priory? It's just a short detour down there!" Joe pointed optimistically downhill into the swirling mist.

Unfortunately, Jeremy was struggling. Like everyone else, his legs were aching and he was overheating. His wet-weather gear was working very well at keeping out the water, but thanks to a thick pullover warmth was building up. Now he dearly wanted to take the pullover off, but to do so meant dropping his rucksack to the floor, taking off his coat, removing the pullover and packing it in his rucksack, before reassembling himself. Altogether too much trouble! Also causing concern was the hood that he desperately wanted to keep on his head as Jeremy didn't want his long hair getting wet. Unfortunately, the string in the hood had retracted into its tube and Jeremy couldn't pull it tight. In short, he was concentrating on walking and the last thing he wanted to do was detour to look at historical artefacts. His reply was short, cutting and effectively stopped Joseph from pursuing the matter.

"Don't talk. I don't have the energy to listen anymore," was all he said.

By now the walkers were entering a wooded area on the side of a hill. The track angled upwards and was slightly muddy and slippery. At the top, the footpath meandered along in stunted birch trees between wood and grass paddocks. Emerging in the mist were the masts of a transmitter station, but there was no sign of other human beings. At a gateway on the edge of the woods, Robert consulted the map and even grabbed his compass.

"We go that way on to moorland. We've got to stick to the track 'cos the mist is thick and we could easily get lost!" he yelled to the assembled group.

Chris added his concerns. "Nobody is to wander off! We've got to be able to see everyone. This is one of those days people could go in different directions and lose each other. Rob, you're in front with the map. Andrew, are you OK at the back?"

Andrew confirmed he was OK bringing up the rear and a well-disciplined group set off over Scarth Moor. The track descended down a slippery and muddy grassy bank before emerging on to a small road. Robert confidently led the way down and across the road and into a wood consisting of deciduous trees against the track, but young larch trees higher up the slopes. This level and sheltered section of the walk seemed to suit the hikers and considerable progress was made in a short time. The damp mist was still all around them, but water droplets no longer stung their faces as they had up on the hills.

"When are we having a break?" shouted Jeremy. "Come on, make it soon, I want to get rid of me pullover and I'm thirsty."

"There's a river coming up, Scugdale Beck it's called. We can stop there, not long, honest," replied Robert, ever the one to urge the group to cover more ground.

Some confusion occurred as the hikers descended over a wet grass field. A Cleveland Way sign at the gate sent the group across the field but halfway over the mist closed in. As the track was indistinct, it was left to Robert to line his map north/south and find the direction with his compass. At the bottom of the paddock was another gate leading to a wooded descent and a ford crossing a stream, with a small foot bridge to one side. At this point a halt was called and Jeremy was at last able to adjust his clothing.

Chris took the opportunity to eat an orange he had purchased the previous night in the village. He proceeded to throw orange peel into Scugdale Beck, something that Andrew was not going to let happen.

"Don't chuck orange peel in the river, Chris, it looks really bad! Just stick it in a side pocket and put it in a bin or bury it," Andrew said, obviously annoyed to see blatant littering of such a beautiful place.

"Get lost, Andrew. Orange peel is biodegradable, so what does it matter? It's only going to be visible for a week or two."

"Yeah, but people will walk past here and see what you've left, won't they? It's not on," Andrew replied, obviously getting angry.

Chris ignored the warning signs and continued despoiling the English countryside. He even smiled at the other walkers, as if goading Andrew to respond.

It took a lot to get Andrew to lose his temper. In fact, Andrew had never been seen by any of the group to commit an act of violence of any sort, hence the incessant teasing that generally accompanied him through life. The perpetrators simply never expected any retaliation. However, today was different. Maybe Andrew was tired, maybe the time had come to make a stand for Britain's diminishing countryside. Whatever it was, Chris didn't know what had hit him! One minute he was standing throwing orange peel into the stream, the next he was sprawled on the road with a very angry Andrew Price standing waiting for him to get up. No punch had been thrown, but as Chris was top heavy due to his rucksack, a powerful push was enough to result in him being ignominiously knocked over. Instantly, Chris lost his temper and with a roar attempted to get up. This time, Andrew only had to stand and watch as Chris overbalanced and went headfirst into a muddy bank. By the time Chris finally stood up, obviously intending to continue the fight, the rest of the expedition had woken up to what was happening and secured the two protagonists, preventing the battle from continuing. Andrew was quite relieved to be restrained as he had never had a real fight before, so he instantly started to laugh through sheer relief! The rest of the group started laughing, too, because they had never witnessed an incensed Andrew before and all over some orange peel. Hilarious! Interestingly, the only person not laughing was Chris! Mainly because the remains of his orange were now being swept downstream in the fast flowing water. As Chris was usually the one laughing on his own at such traumatic incidents, the situation was made all the funnier for everyone else.

Andreas stepped forward and diffused the situation by calming the two 'friends' and forcing a reconciliatory handshake. As the hikers marched off again, Joe turned to Andrew and asked what biodegradable meant. Naturally, Andrew enlightened him while making the valid point that lots of things were biodegradable, such as wrapping paper and dead bodies, but you wouldn't consider leaving them littered alongside a walking track in the North York Moors National Park!

Even though the seven hikers had only been stationary for ten minutes during their break at Scugdale Beck, tendrils of cold had penetrated their clothing. Jeremy felt it most and he made sure the rest of the hikers were well aware of his predicament. Without his pullover on he was now freezing cold! Of course, with his pullover on he would have returned to an overheated condition and so it was not an easy situation. The only solution was to get moving, which is why Jeremy moved up the column to encourage Robert to keep up a good pace.

The track zigzagged through Heathwaite and around the bottom edge of woodland, alongside which could be seen old mine tailings. Next was the steep rise up the nose of Knolls End. This climb fixed Jeremy's cold problem and briefly returned him, and everyone else, to a condition of overheating. At the top of the hill the map and compass resolved direction again although, on reflection, the route into open moorland was the only logical one after studying the map. Now conditions really did deteriorate to such an extent that the walkers gathered in the lee of the ridge on Faceby Bank to put pullovers and jumpers back on.

As the expedition approached the clearings made in the heather for the Carlton Bank Gliding Club, the rain began to pour. Not downwards, as you might expect, but sideways. The wind was howling and the horizontal rain was stinging their exposed faces. Any view the walkers might have been anticipating across the open countryside to Teesside was totally obscured. Frankly, at no point was their visibility greater than 50 yards.

For Andrew, still bringing up the rear, the conditions produced a thrilling sense of euphoria. The weather was dangerous, exhilarating and challenging. Their wet-weather gear was holding up under the strain and everyone seemed to be enjoying the experience.

The descent to the Lord Stones proved hazardous, as this edge of the moor seemed to be catching the brunt of the wind and rain. The track was steep, rocky and ill-defined with a number of possible routes apparent over the shale left behind from the old alum workings. However, in the lee of Cringle Moor on the ascent, conditions eased slightly – enough for conversation to be resumed.

"That was fantastic on that last hill, with the wind and rain!" an excited Andreas announced.

"You're right, 'Dreas. It hurt, but it was a thrill," said Chris.

"You're all talking like there's no more hilltops to be on!" said Andrew quizzically. "When Rob and I looked at the map last night we counted five descents and ascents before Hasty Bank. So far we've only had three!"

"Is he right, Rob? I'm getting seriously tired," admitted a bedraggled Jeremy, who had failed miserably to keep his hair dry.

"Andy's right, we've two more dips and rises after this climb and even then we have to decide what we're going to do about camping tonight, which frankly means at least one more descent if we come back off Hasty Bank ."

"Can we camp on the side of Hasty Bank?" asked Martin, somewhat disturbed to hear how many ups and downs still faced the explorers.

"That does sound the best idea to me," added Andrew, who had a secret desire to camp on the moors, in the wilds so to speak. "Maybe we could slip behind Hasty Bank on to one of the farms, at least then we're not as exposed as on the very top of the moors. I don't reckon we should camp where the wind could get up, like back on Carlton Bank."

"I'll go along with that!" announced Joe. "But when are we having lunch? I'm hungry and I need a pee!"

Robert studied the map and pointed to the small valley just after Cringle Moor. "I know it's late, but if we can get over there we'll find a sheltered spot for a break. That'll keep us going nice and fresh while we find somewhere to camp."

The weather deteriorated again on top of the next moor and a very tired group of walkers descended into the col between Cringle and Cold Moor. In the shelter of a stone wall, the walkers made themselves comfortable and tucked into bread, cheese, fruitcake and apples. Chocolate bars became dessert as did Kendal Mint Cake, which was one of the purchases Jeremy had made on behalf of the group. The latter seemed to give a welcome energy boost on what was proving to be a very energetic day.

Andrew was getting anxious. "Come on, fellas, its three o'clock! We've got to keep going."

With their rucksacks back on, a damp group of walkers set off again.

"Do you realise we haven't met anyone all day!" said Martin. "It's brilliant – we've the whole Yorkshire Moors to ourselves!" With that Martin began to sing a well-known refrain, which, one by one, everyone joined in with:

"I love to go a-wandering,
Along the mountain track
And as I go, I love to sing,
My knapsack on my back.
Val-deri Val-dera
Val-deri Val-dera ha ha ha ha ha
Val-deri Val-dera.
My knapsack on my back."

That moment, with the wind and rain beginning to increase on the top of Cold Moor and the sound of seven walkers belting out that classic mountaineers' song, stood as a unique moment of freedom. Joseph couldn't help thinking this encapsulated exactly what walking the Cleveland Way meant to him. Never again would the seven young men from Leicestershire experience such elation in the face of the extremes of nature – not together as a group of friends, anyway. Never again would their spirits fly so high and be so free from responsibility. If only he could stop fretting about what his beloved Yvonne was up to!

Suddenly, Joseph ran forward and climbed a rocky knoll next to the walking path. His scrambling and frantic movements halted all the walkers in their tracks and they found themselves gathering informally in front of him, as Joe delivered lines from Shakespeare's *King Lear*. Joseph was in the midst of revision for his mock A-level exam in English literature and he realised how appropriate these Shakespearean words were in their current circumstances. Despite the wind and rain, he struck the classic actor's pose and proceeded to dominate the elements by shouting out his lines.

"Blow, winds and crack your cheeks! Rage! Blow! You cataracts and hurricanoes, spout. Till you have drenched our steeples."

The assembled walkers burst into applause, to which Joe took a gracious bow before loudly announcing: "But there's more! Now, from John Milton's *Paradise Lost* let me just add, in case the weather is dampening your spirits, the following refrain: All is not lost, the unconquerable will, and study of revenge, immortal hate and the courage never to submit or yield." Again Joe took a bow, but this line left the rest of the group pondering the full implication.

Robert broke the spell and returned things to normality by simply saying loudly: "Well, thanks, Joe!" His twin brother added the final nail of sarcasm by adding: "Yes, thanks, mate. That really helps!" Still, the literary moment had proved inspirational for Joseph and just for a while he had forgotten about Yvonne!

Onward the walkers went, down into Garfit Gap. Here the weather deteriorated further. There was no increase in rain but visibility decreased and the wind picked up. Silently, the hikers marched yet again upwards. By now legs were seriously fatigued, but there was no choice but to carry on.

Out of the mist ahead strange apparitions began to take shape. Huge monoliths of rock materialised in front of them like a large natural ruin.

"It's the Wainstones!" Robert said to the walker behind him. One by one, all the walkers turned to tell the hiker behind them the name of the stony shapes appearing ahead. The whole process was like some wet, cold and bedraggled game of Chinese whispers.

"Wow, they're seriously weird aren't they?" Joe said to the assembled group, when they finally gathered in the dubious shelter of the stones. "I mean, they emerged out of the mist like they were moving. It was made spookier by the fact I had no idea they were here." Joe spoke as he shifted his weight from side to side, obviously hurting under the pressure of his rucksack.

Jeremy was suffering, too, with aching legs and feet and a cold head. "Come on, fellas, we've gotta find a campsite, this is bloody hard work."

Robert offered the map for everyone to look at and consensus was reached to leave the track once on top of Hasty Bank and head south across open moor to reach one of the two farms shown on the south side of the ridge.

"Let's stick close together as we cross the moor. I know the contours don't look close enough to be real steep, but you never know. In this mist we could still get lost and it's that cold I don't reckon you'd last long out here on your own," Chris added. No one contradicted him.

Above the Wainstones the track began to level out. After half a mile or so, the seven hikers left the safety of the Cleveland Way and started out across open moorland. In no time at all, the mist obliterated any trace of landmark and direction. Only Robert's compass and a slight slope to the south allowed any semblance of navigation. Blundering across the heather seemed to last forever and was made more difficult by the early approach of dusk. Several boulders were negotiated and some steep banks descended before a stone wall came into view. Once over the wall and in the small paddock beyond, the going got easier. The grass was short, courtesy of a large number of black-faced sheep, a lot of them with lambs at foot. Tractor ruts led the hikers to a five-bar gate hinged with orange baler twine. Once through the gate, the increasingly cold and tired walkers followed the tractor tracks in the blind hope they would lead to habitation. Finally, emerging through the mist appeared the dull grey outline of farm buildings alongside which was a stone house with a yellowish light burning behind a downstairs window. Civilisation had been relocated!

Chapter 9

A Night on the Wild Side

It wasn't their intention to frighten the occupants of the house, but that's exactly what the seven hikers managed to achieve! Mind you, it's hardly surprising that the mother and daughter – who were the only occupants of that bleak, windswept cottage – were anything other than frightened! The young girl opened the door after hearing Andrew's rather timid knock. She was confronted by seven bedraggled desperados, the ones at the front dripping water over the row of muddy wellingtons standing in the porch. Hardly surprising then, that, she slammed the door and ran back inside with a scream.

"You handled that well, Andrew!" said Robert, with a sarcastic smile.

"No wonder you haven't got a girlfriend, Andy! Does this happen every time women look at you!" asked Martin, who was standing half in and half out of the porch.

A voice at the rear yelled: "What's happ'ning?"

Robert turned around and yelled back: "Don't ask, normal service will be resumed as soon as possible!" With that, Robert leaned forward and knocked more forcibly than Andrew's first attempt.

This time, the lady of the house came to the door. Tentatively, the door was opened about twelve inches and a wind-blown, red, female face appeared. A face that was obviously anxious and not used to large troupes of visitors just on dusk.

114

"Now then, can I 'elp ye?" she nervously enquired.

Andrew was still at the front, so he became spokesman. "Sorry to disturb you at this time of the evening and in this weather, but we're walking the Cleveland Way and frankly we've run out of time to find a campsite."

"Well, I've no room fer all o' ye in t'farmhouse, I'm sorry lads," she responded.

"No, no, you don't understand. We wouldn't dream of asking you to do that! No, we just wanted to ask permission to camp in one of your paddocks. I'm from a farm as well and, well, we wouldn't want to set up tents or anything without making sure the owners of the land were happy. We won't leave any rubbish or anything. All we would ask is to fill our water bottles from your tap if that's OK?"

With that, the door opened fully and a somewhat relieved female farmer smiled at the hikers. In the background, behind an old wooden table on a flagstone floored kitchen stood the young daughter, still not quite comfortable with the herd of young men standing outside her front door.

"Aye, o' course ye can camp! There's a sheltered spot at t'back o' t'paddock behind yon barn. There's even an old wooden shed in't corner ye can use if ye wants. It's a bare earth floor, but ye could stick yer packs in it if ye wants. Like ye said though, don't go leavin' any rubbish as I'm sure ye knows, it only teks one plastic bag to kill a sheep or a beast if they eats it. There's a bin next t'porch 'ere. Just put yer litter in that in't mornin'!"

Offering sincere thanks, the walkers turned and walked into the paddock behind the barn. The only way to locate the sheltered spot with the small wooden shed was to walk around against the wall. Visibility was getting worse, so finding the campsite was a challenge. Eventually, the paddock dipped into a corner where a small wooden skillion had been made using the corner of the field as two of its walls. The roof was corrugated iron and the floor bare earth strewn with sheep droppings. The only way in was to bend low through a small opening and inside there wasn't room to stand.

Andreas went inside and got to work. Using a piece of planking he scraped sheep manure over to one side, ejecting it outside under some loose timber. While he made the shed serviceable, the rest of the hikers pitched the tents. Fortunately, the farmer had been correct in saying this area was sheltered. While the wind and mist still swirled around, conditions were much better than in the middle of the paddock or up on the moors. At Robert's insistence, the tents were erected in a circle so all the entrances faced one another. Sleeping bags were rolled out, but packs were carried to the shelter of the small wooden shed and handed to Andreas, who lined them up alongside one of the stone walls. Finally, the walkers huddled inside the cramped shed with the wind whistling in through loose boards on the front and one of the sides.

The light was all but gone as gas stoves were lit and cooking the evening meal became the priority.

Jeremy announced the culinary line-up of the night's 'gustation'.

"We're finishing off the tins of beef stew and with them we'll have Yeoman dehydrated mashed potatoes, tinned peas and tinned carrots. We've got bread, jam and custard tarts for pudding."

"Sounds fantastic!" said a drooling Joseph, his sentiments agreed with by everyone present. "As long as we rehydrate the dehydrated, it'll be a meal fit for a king and as long as the tinned stew doesn't biodegrade in Andreas' or Robert's stomachs afterwards, we'll all survive the experience!"

"It's to be hoped we don't get a repeat performance of what happened the other night!" added Jeremy who, like Andrew and Chris, had spent the night with his head outside the tent thanks to Robert and Andreas.

"There's enough wind blowing here tonight to dissipate nuclear fallout, let alone anything Andreas or Robert can produce!" said Martin with a grin.

"We can sit in here after we've eaten and drink tea and eat chocolate by torch light!" added Joe. "Whatever we do, it's nice to be out of the weather and sitting down."

Outside the rickety shed the light was fading fast. The wind began to ease, but a thick cold mist hung around Hasty Bank that torch light couldn't penetrate. Inside the building, the roar of four camping stoves broke the silence as did the ongoing chatter from seven tired and hungry young men. With plates of food distributed, the stoves were put to work again heating water for very welcome cups of steaming hot tea. Dirty plates were put outside the lean-to to be sorted out in the morning, nobody being too keen to move from the relative warmth of the huddle within the confines of their refuge. Despite still being clad in the same wet-weather clothing, boots and socks they had worn all day, this was comfort indeed!

Suddenly, a strange sound could be heard passing in an arc above their heads. A sort of buzzing the like of which none of the group had heard before and only one of whom could explain.

"What's that weird sound?" asked Joe.

"Believe it or not, it's a bird!" replied Andrew. "But I've never heard it before in real life. I've only heard it on an LP of bird song Dad got me."

"You mean there's LPs of bird song! I bet you wear your brown jacket when you walk in the shop asking for one of them!" Jeremy added sarcastically.

"That's nothing!" said Chris. "My old man's got an LP of steam train noises. Different classes of engine on the straight, going through tunnels and around bends!"

"You're all going round the bend if you ask me!" muttered Joe. "Come on Andy, what bird makes that noise? I can't imagine how it gets its beak around a sound like that."

"It's not made vocally, Joe. I'll give two squares of chocolate to any of you who can tell me how it's doing it, never mind what sort of bird it is!" challenged Andrew, enjoying the bird banter.

Robert dragged the conversation downwards again. "Whatever species it is, it's been eating beef stew and it's farting its way over the sky: sort of a bird version of jet propulsion!"

Outside, the bird continued to criss-cross above the paddock, making the strange vibratory sounds.

"I reckon my chocolate's safe! The bird is a snipe. It's a long-beaked wading bird, a bit like the common sandpiper we saw on the first day. We do get 'em in the 'Vale' back home, but only in the winter. They breed up here, on and around the moors. What he's doing is showing off to attract a female, like you lot when you're dancing at a disco. The difference is he's got two peculiar tail feathers that stick out either side of his backside. He holds them stiffly as he passes through the air and they vibrate – that's what you can hear, two vibrating tail feathers!"

"That's incredible! God works in mysterious ways, his wonders to perform!" said Joe.

"Get on, Joe! God's got nothing to do with it," said Andrew. "It's just evolution. The females pick out the ones with the best display and the ones who make the most noise, and slowly but surely, you end with this noisy little fella evolving. He's just showing he's got the best snipe genes!"

Jeremy was quick to comment, desperately trying to dig laughs from the conversation.

"It's all to do with jeans, Joe. That's why I wear 'Loons'. That flash of red from below the knee on either side of my leg, in the flare, sends 'em wild, mate. I'm fighting women off like that snipe will be later on!"

Joe was more interested in pursuing the religious argument.

"So, Andy, are you an atheist? Don't you believe in God?"

"That's right, Joe, I'm an atheist just like you!"

"But I'm not an atheist am I! I believe in God."

Andrew continued with a well-rehearsed line he had heard his grandfather use one Sunday lunch time. The wonderful thing about growing up in the Price household was the frank and free-flowing debates that occurred during meal times. Andrew's mother had been terrified by the intensity of such discussion when she first joined her future husband's family for meals in the early stages of their courtship. She had mistakenly taken debate for argument and genuinely thought the family was wracked by dissention.

"Do you believe in the Hindu gods then, Joe? What about the Muslim faith? What about Thor the god of lightning, do you believe in him?" asked an earnest Andrew.

Joe was adamant in his response: "No, I don't believe in any of that, they've all got it wrong, haven't they?"

Andrew persisted. "So, you too are an atheist then, at least for any of those gods that aren't yours! The only difference between me and you, Joe, is that I'm atheist for one more god than you are!"

"That's not right, you can't be that simplistic. My faith is complex, and anyway, it's all written in the Bible!"

"Maybe not everything written in your Bible is true then,

Joe!" said Andrew, just for once holding his own with Joseph, but acutely aware that cold logic would soon give way to song lyrics and artistic flowery rhetoric, the likes of which Andrew's scientific mind failed to keep pace with, or even comprehend.

Andreas and Chris also studied biology with Andrew. Unlike Andrew, they hadn't participated in theological discussion with Joe before that night. The twins and Jeremy, on the other hand, were like Joe in that they went beyond 'youth club' and embraced 'youth fellowship': The overtly religious part of local organised youth activity.

Andreas aligned himself with Andrew and asked: "Do you believe in Noah's Ark then, Joe?"

"If it's in the Bible then it must be true," was Joe's response.

"So, Joe, were Australia's marsupials on the Ark with all the usual lions and stuff?" Andreas persisted, beginning a line of argument gleaned from his biology teaching father.

"If it's in the Bible then it must be true!" was again Joe's emphatic response.

Andreas too was on a 'roll' of logic. "Show me any reference to kangaroos in the Bible, or any pictures of kangaroos getting on the Ark that you can prove were painted before Captain Cook found Australia and I'll accept your 'God made everything' argument, Joe! Even if kangaroos and wombats and all the other marsupial species were on the Ark, how the hell did they all concentrate themselves in Australia when they hopped off that big boat after it washed up on Mount Ararat in Turkey! It's just nonsense!"

Joe gave his standard reply. "God works in mysterious ways, his wonders to perform!"

An exasperated Andrew responded, "Now who's being simplistic, Joe! That answer is a cop out and doesn't make a proper scientific argument!"

Robert, who had been quietly listening to the debate, interjected. "We're going to get nowhere arguing about religion and I don't want to spend tonight in deep philosophical discussion. For what it's worth, I reckon your religion, or lack of it, should be a personal thing. You know, private – between you and your god. I reckon showing it, or making it institutionalised, as in all the big churches and organised religion generally, destroys it. The closest I got to a religious feeling lately is when I was up on the moors today. You know, in the mist and rain fighting my way over the heather to get here, and you know what, that's good enough for me!"

Andrew replied, "You've got a point, Rob. Listening to that snipe does it for me! That's the closest I get to a religious experience. Oh, and up on the hills today, like you."

"It's sport for me!" added Chris. "That feeling when the shuttlecock slams down on the opposite court and you gain a point, or when the ball thumps into the back of the net. Yeah, that's my religious feeling."

"I know what you mean!" said Jeremy. "Scoring goals does it for me, and singing in the band!"

Eyes turned to Andreas for his religious experience. "For me it's when the cable on the glider goes taut and you begin to move forward. Then it's up into the sky. Wow!"

Martin was the only one left. "For me, like Joe, it's music and, of course, Janet, but she's not mine anymore."

Andrew and Chris looked sheepishly downward at this remark, only too aware of their responsibility for Martin's predicament.

Jeremy brought up the subject of football, which suited Chris down to the ground.

"Who do you reckon will be top of the First Division then, Jez?" Chris asked.

Jeremy replied, "It's hard to imagine Liverpool winning now after that loss on Monday to Sheffield United. So I suppose it'll be Leeds at the top. I reckon we'll actually see your Man United drop out the First Division Martin! Maybe Middlesbrough moving up?"

Chris was in his element. "The FA Cup has been interesting hasn't it? Liverpool are going to win and frankly they deserve it. I don't want Newcastle to get anywhere after that bloomin' riot at St James's Park against Notts Forest. Talk about intimidation!"

Jeremy was quick to add that, despite it being Newcastle United's crowds who had caused the rumpus, Newcastle football team had done well to win. Not only had they lost a player, whose sending off had prompted the riot, but they had recovered to win, despite being two goals down.

A change of subject was needed because only Chris, Jeremy, and to a lesser extent, Martin, showed any real interest in football.

"What about girls then? We haven't mentioned many females on this trip!" observed Robert.

Joe looked up and appeared suddenly enthused. "Tell you what, there's some lovely girls in our English class aren't there, Jez? And we're the only blokes! There's ten gorgeous females and just us two!"

"Go on then! Who do you rate as gorgeous? List them – let's see if any of us know 'em."

"All right then! There's Sylvana for a start off!"

Jeremy was quickly into the fray. "God, she's gorgeous isn't she? Especially when a couple of buttons come undone on her blouse on a summer's day!"

"She does that deliberately, Jez! She knows you're looking at her! What about Belinda Jacobs? She takes some beating!" added Joe.

Jeremy mouthed ten out of ten and Robert saw him. "No, Jez, she's worth more than ten out of ten, mate. She does maths with me – I've snogged her behind the sports hall! Can you get fifteen out of ten?"

"There's one more ruined woman who'll never be the same again!" observed Martin, well aware of the girl concerned and equally willing to give her a high score! "This reminds me of the bloke asked to judge the beauty contest. He went up to the first girl in the line-up and she gave him a wink. The next girl winked and smiled, the third gave him a hug, the fourth girl gave him a kiss on the cheek and the fifth a full snog on the lips. Which girl did he give the prize to?"

"The fifth, I bet!" said Andreas, hanging on Martin's every word.

"No, Andreas!" Martin added. "He gave the first prize to number twelve!"

As the laughter and ribald comments died back, Jeremy, ever the one for the last laugh, threw in a joke of his own.

"There's this bank manager who advertises for a new teller. Three girls show up. He interviews them one at a time. He says to the first girl: 'Right, you come to work and there's a ten pound note on the floor. What do you do with it?'

"'Well,' she replies. 'I'm a great believer in finders keepers, losers weepers. I would pocket the money for myself.'

"The bank manager shows her out and asks girl number two in. He asks her the exact same question.

"'Well,' she replies. 'I'm a believer in finders keepers, losers weepers, but as I'm working in a bank, I suppose I ought to hand some back. So I'd keep five pounds and give five pounds to the bank.'

"The bank manager shows her out and asks girl number three to come in. Again, he asks the same question.

"'Well,' she replies. 'Obviously it isn't mine so I'd hand it in to the bank.'" At this point Jeremy paused for dramatic effect before asking the assembled males: "So which girl did the bank manager give the job to?"

Andreas jumped in first. "I suppose it's obvious – he'd give the job to the third girl because she's the most honest."

Jeremy delivered the punchline in the same showy style with which he delivered song lyrics. "No! He gave it to the girl with the biggest tits!"

The laughter this joke provoked created a lull in proceedings long enough for the decision to be made to refill the saucepans with water and relight the gas stoves in order to make another hot brew. This time it was all done by torch light, as the day had all but disappeared. Joe was keen to relate a story that would make everyone smile. He had long ago realised that self-deprecating events always brought a laugh from his friends, so he recounted the following tale: "One day when Jez was absent from school, I found myself even more outnumbered than usual in the English class. There was little old me, ten gorgeous girls and Mrs flippin' Robinson." (Everybody huddled in the snug little skillion knew Mrs flippin' Robinson! As ever 'Jesus loves you more than you will know' was whispered under the breath of all those present. God help you though if you ever hummed the tune in front of her, as Jeremy once found out!) "We were studying love poems. Mrs Robinson wanted to open up debate on physical attraction and her gaze fell on me!

"'Well, Joseph, as our token male here today, let us ask your opinion. What do men see in women?' Mrs Robinson quietly asked.

"A ghost of expectation suddenly entered the classroom and I realised all eyes were upon me! I didn't know what to say, so I played for time. 'Sorry, Miss, what did you ask?'

"'Well, Joseph, what does one look for in the opposite sex?'

"I looked around and all the girls were staring at me! They were all waiting for some sophisticated, romantic and enlightening response!"

"Well go on then, did you give 'em one?" asked Martin. Like everyone else he was thoroughly enjoying listening to Joseph who, once in full flow, had a way with words – totally unlike the rest of the group.

"What do mean, Mart? Did he give 'em one? Don't reckon Yvonne would like him doing anything like that!" announced Robert lecherously from the back of the lean-to.

"I'd forgotten all about her!" said Joe in an anguished tone. "Oh, that's terrible. I wish you hadn't reminded me. There's no way I can ring, or anything!"

Martin snapped back at his brother, telling him to shut up about Yvonne and to stop trying to be funny. Then he implored Joe to carry on with his story.

"It was the word sex that threw me! 'What does one look for in the opposite sex?' Honestly, it really threw me and for a while I wished Jeremy was there to share some of the heat!"

"I'd share Sylvana's heat anytime! I bet she was hanging out for your reply," Jeremy added.

"I tried to buy more time. 'What Miss? Could you rephrase the question?' I remember asking. But Mrs Robinson was having none of this time-wasting and her voice changed tone, to the one where you know times run out.

"'Mr Krinn, please could you give us the benefit of your wisdom. What is it you first notice in a female you are attracted to?'

"I felt cornered and the words from the Stones' 'Street Fighting Man' slipped into my mind. You know, 'what can a poor boy do'. I took a deep breath and uttered the first thing that came into my mind. 'Legs... err... long legs!'"

There was uproar in the little shed because everyone present realised just how disappointed Mrs Robinson would have been for the 'artistic' Joseph to have given such a crass and base reply. For a few minutes, the friction produced by laughter warmed the cramped hikers in the lean-to.

Back in the classroom, on that fateful day, no tutor's discipline strategy needed to be applied to gain the class's full attention, as the words Joe had just blurted out bounced around the school room. The look of disappointment on the teacher's face was matched only by the sheer open-mouthed surprise that was palpable on several girls' faces.

Joe continued his tale: "In an attempt to keep the lesson flowing, Mrs Robinson, in her most haughty tone of disapproval, looked at me and said. 'Maybe her beautiful face, or engaging smile, well-groomed hair, her cheery personality or playful disposition, mmm?' I expected the girls to laugh but there was just silence! They were all watching me for an answer! I remember saying: 'Yes, of course, Miss. That goes without saying.'

"Honestly, I could feel marks falling from my grades in English! Then she said something and I knew I could get a laugh. You would have been proud of me, Jez! She looked at me and said – and I'm not kidding – this is exactly what she said: 'I had expected something a little higher than legs, Joseph.' I couldn't believe my luck! I just added, 'Yes, you're right, Miss... small breasts!'"

Jeremy, amongst paroxysms of laughter, could really picture the magic of this scene as he was usually there in the class. "Brilliant Joe! I bet the girls loved that!"

"Well, that's the odd thing, Jez. Sure there was a ripple of laughter, but you know Rita on the front row?" Jeremy acknowledged with a yes and Robert yelled 'five out of ten', just to remind everyone of his superior knowledge of all things female. "Well, Rita astonishingly exclaimed: 'You're so shallow, Joe.' That threw me for a while, but Sylvana came hilariously to my rescue by saying out loud, with Mrs Robinson in the class mind you! 'Shush, Rita. I'm scoring really well on this list so far!' Everyone sniggered, the debate on love poems collapsed, but luckily we were saved by the bell and I almost ran out of the class just to get away!"

Jeremy, despite being absent from the class on the day in question, was determined to glean some of the laughter for himself in front of the 'camp fire' audience. "Oh, that explains why, when I came back the next day, the whole of the upper sixth were wearing miniskirts."

But Robert was in fine form and was able to grab the last laugh by adding to Jeremy's comment. "Hopefully not the males!" he flippantly interjected. Another round of laughter echoed through the little sheep shed.

On a roll, Joe then recalled a funnier event two years earlier in a maths class. "Do you remember how they used to set students and differentiate by sitting us in rows – a bit like the Roman army, though in reverse?" Joe began. "Mr Hodgson would put the most able mathematicians on the front row nearest to him, as they were the only ones on his wavelength. Then he put the middling sort, like me, in the middle and those he despaired of passing GCE to the rear of the classroom."

Joe continued: "I was so fortunate; if I ever got stuck I could poke the calculating machine who sat on the front row just ahead of me. That's Randolph Marson, you know the American who was in school just for one term. He was an absolute genius – no wonder the yanks were the first to land on the Moon if they can produce geniuses like Randolph Marson!

Anyway, whenever I was stuck in maths, I could poke my way to a higher grade by asking Randolph the answer."

Jeremy had been in the maths class with Joe, sitting alongside him in the middle ranks, as it were.

"I remember you doing it, Joe, and I remember the one major drawback in your strategy: you really got told off, didn't you? Those times old Hodgson saw you do it! You were straight in detention if I remember rightly, sometimes with the girl behind you!"

"You're not kidding, Jez! You see the system had its rewards and merits because behind me was Debbie Cammack."

"Debbie Cammack! I remember her. She wasn't Miss World, but you had a thing for her, Joe, didn't you? At least for a while." Jeremy added.

"She had really sharp fingers; I know that 'cos she used to poke me for the same answers I had just poked Randolph for! So we had a system. Whatever Deb needed – arithmetically speaking – could be provided with one proviso, we must avoid the ever present danger of Hodgson seeing us and putting us in detention!" Joe continued.

Jeremy started laughing. "I know what's coming! I remember this, so funny! Don't worry, Joe, I won't say any more. You tell it as it was – hilarious!"

Joseph continued: "The pitfall was to poke at the wrong time – when the teacher was looking was the main hazard to be avoided at all costs. Backs could become sore and patience stretched to its limits when Mr Hodgson was looking in our direction. Speaking or turning around carried the death sentence, at least we acted as if it did. Then it happened. It was an afternoon in May during the termly maths test when it all came to a head. Debbie was more frustrated than usual and the test was demanding my absolute concentration. My vexation over the test was more than matched by my sore back. Debbie would not give up. Question four proved particularly difficult for both of us. Hodgson was at his most vigilant; totally match fit as it were, limbering up for the detention home run! It wasn't a good time to turn around, especially as I couldn't even hope to erase the look of disappointment on her face when I admitted I didn't know the answer. Having Deb look up to me – thanks to those blue eyes – was one of the highlights of my day. I didn't dare involve Randolph. When it came to geek points, in the eyes of the girls at least, he was king. Only the jester of humour could topple his royal crown. The joker in me longed to trounce the king and the opportunity was coming my way. On this occasion, the volcano awoke from its dormant state. Debbie erupted, stood to her full height of five foot five inches and exclaimed loudly so all could appreciate it: 'Joe, if you can't give me the answer why don't you just get Randy for me?"

The little shed erupted into laughter to the extent that tea was spilt.

Joe continued: "That's not all. I couldn't look her in the eye – there was nowhere to run except to the punchline. As Hodgson expelled us from the classroom, I quipped as loudly as Debbie: 'I'll do my best, Debs, but it is a maths lesson and a test to boot!'"

Joe had failed another maths test, but had passed the test that matters to all teenagers – the humour exam.

Joseph began to realise he had been hogging the floor. "Come on then, someone else tell some funny tales. I'm getting a sore throat."

Andrew decided to emulate Joe with some self-deprecation. "All right, I'll tell you something you might find funny. Looking back, I find it funny anyway, even though the laugh's on me. When I was about twelve or thirteen I read somewhere that ivy kills trees, so I decided to carry a saw with me on my bike so I could 'save' any trees I thought were being throttled by ivy growing up them. Every morning I push-biked past a house in Harby that had an ash tree in the middle of the garden with ivy growing up it. The stem of the ivy was as thick as my leg – it was massive! I decided to save the tree and so one misty morning, at about quarter to eight, I parked the bike and leapt the fence. Then I started sawing. An upstairs window on the owner's house was slid up and open and a big hairy bloke – he had no shirt on – yelled at me: 'Oy! What you doing?'

"I just stood up with me saw in me hand and said: 'Who, me?'

"'Who the hell else do you think I mean?'

"'I dunno?'

"'Of course I mean you, you pillock! What the hell are you doing cutting my bloody tree down at quarter to eight in the morning? You'll wreck my bloody car!'

"'No, you don't understand!'

"'Too bloody right I don't understand!'

"'No, I'm not cutting your tree down: I'm just cutting the ivy!'

"The hairy fella then turned round and addressed someone else in the room; I suppose it was his wife. I could hear what he was saying. I could plainly hear him ask the other person: 'Do we want our ivy cutting off the tree?'

"The female voice inside said: 'No, we bloody don't!'

"The bloke then swung back around and stuck his head out the window and yelled: 'Piss off!'

"I was out of there in no time, I can tell you!"

When the laughter died down from this revelation, Martin took the floor. "I've two revelations from school!"

"Not the double-decker bus story again, we all know about that! Or the girlfriends under the stage, we all know about that as well!" chided Jeremy, changing position on the floor as stiffness replaced comfort.

Martin continued: "No, neither of those. In the first year at Belvoir High School I was wandering round at lunchtime and decided it would be an idea to try to push a teacher's car into the long-jump pit. So, me and Peter Kemp tried to push a few, but none would move, until, that is, we gave Fagin's car a shove. Chris and Joe, you didn't go to Belvoir High so for your benefit Fagin was an old and wrinkled English teacher who smoked whenever he could and spent the lessons telling weird little stories. Actually, looking back, he wasn't much of a teacher, more an entertainer! Anyway, his car was only a little Fiat and he hadn't put the handbrake on. Mind you, Pete and me couldn't quite get it to the long jump, but we were pushing hard. Next thing, Gilbert Jones and his mates from fourth year rocked up and offered to help! Well, with them it was easy and we soon had the car sitting in the middle of the long-jump pit! Trouble was, we'd been seen and we were all sent to Mr Walbank's office to face the music. He strode out and confronted us: 'Right, who's the ring leader then?'

"All these big, tough fourth years pointed at me! I was a midget, being a first year. Old Walbank went ballistic!"

"'Don't go blaming Jenkins – he's only a first year – I bet you're behind this, Jones! Right, Jenkins, I want you and Kemp back to your classrooms. Take heed, lads, stay away from Jones and his dubious colleagues in future. As for you, Jones, and your motley crew, four weeks detention!'

"As you can imagine, I was glad to miss detention, but Gilbert Jones and his mates gave me a right hiding in the bus queue that night!"

Martin then entertained the hikers with the story of him and Robert mixing up the male and female rabbits, again at Belvoir High School. Male and female rabbits were kept well apart from each other in separate hutches. After the twins had carried out some reorganisation one lunch hour, the rabbits were well able to do what came naturally, ensuring the birth of many more rabbits than the school could cope with several weeks later. Despite a campaign of threats and intimidation levelled at all students by Mr Walbank in assembly when the switch was finally noticed, the perpetrators were never caught. In fact, the revelation by Martin of his involvement ended ongoing speculation as to who the culprits were, which was of great interest to Jeremy, Andreas and Andrew, who had, of course, been at the school at the time.

Martin's tale from the past reminded Jeremy of an epic bit of exploration when a group of village lads in Long Clawson decided to crawl through the 'Sands' in the storm water drain. The 'Sands' was an area of houses, shops and pubs in the centre of that long Leicestershire village. The boys knew where a stream, which in the past used to flow through the 'Sands', had been directed into a large drainpipe, but they had no idea where it emerged. With a truly brave spirit of adventure, the six schoolboys crawled into the pipe with no room to turn around and no hope of backing out. Brave spirits because none of them knew where, or indeed if, the pipe emerged into daylight again! Hardly surprisingly, this story was shared by the Jenkins twins, who were very much a part of this endeavour as well. After three terrifying hours of crawling and feeling their way (feeling because naturally nobody had had time to get a torch!) a much relieved and triumphant group of filthy schoolboys emerged at the bottom of a ditch in a paddock below the village.

Andreas and Chris were strangely quiet. Both were feeling

intimidated by the 'youth club' clique, who seemed to share a lot of dubious and sometimes exaggerated experiences. Both were also too sensible to be involved in such outlandish and foolhardy exploits. It was a safety issue with Chris. The caution exhibited by his father in all things, except sporting exertion, kept his exploits firmly on the straight and narrow.

For Andreas, time was precious. At weekends, his father had him working in the piggery. His bit of boyhood comradeship came through the Air Training Corps. Recently, he had divulged some of the antics that occurred when he and his fellow aviators went on camp. Something involving naked young men and long socks placed over appendages! Unfortunately, Andreas had confided in Chris and Chris had distributed Andreas's confidential information to those who wanted to hear. Actually, he had also spread the word to those who didn't want to hear it, so great was Chris's desire to gain kudos from his friend's confidences. Andreas was, therefore, quite content to sit and listen, hoping not to draw attention to himself or prompt another round of 'what size socks have you got on today 'Dreas?' from Chris. Andreas wasn't going to risk exposing himself to that amount of ridicule, certainly not in the company of some relatively new acquaintances, into which category Joseph, Jeremy and to a slightly lesser extent the Jenkins twins, fell.

"Isn't it about bedtime then?" asked Jeremy, who seemed to be finding it difficult to get comfortable.

Robert brought everyone's minds back to the walk. "Tomorrow we have another long walk over the moors, but this time it looks flatter. We end up above Great Ayton. It's about the same distance as today. Where we will camp tomorrow night is anyone's guess though!"

Andrew remembered some more from the guidebook. "We

walk past a big monument to Captain Cook tomorrow at Great Ayton. He was born or lived round there, apparently. Tell you what though, I really hope the weather improves. It's getting pretty bad wearing wet socks and we haven't got unlimited spare clothes."

This sentiment was agreed with by everyone. Slowly, the hikers left the refuge of the wooden shelter and, with tired, aching limbs, groped their way to their tents. The tea had worked its way through their systems and all the hikers lined up behind the tents for a pee before the long drawn out process of getting undressed and into sleeping bags could begin. The presence of the lean-to shed paid dividends, as wet-weather clothes could be placed in there for the night. The absence of rucksacks in the tents made for a spacious night's sleep. Even the continuing calls of sheep and the intermittent drumming display of the snipe failed to keep anyone awake for longer than ten minutes.

Chapter 10

Hasty Bank to Great Ayton

The first thing the hikers noticed when they awoke the next morning was that the weather hadn't improved. In fact, if anything conditions were far worse. Yesterday's moisture was provided by skeins of mist, today's by torrents of rain. First up and at it was Andreas, who in the mornings was becoming an inspiration to all. Actually, on this particular day the hikers had overslept due to being exhausted and to the diminished daylight illuminating the sodden campsite. Andreas found himself up and about at 8.30am, which was just as well because at that moment the lady farmer approached the campers carrying a jug of milk. She spotted Andreas.

"Mornin'! Did ye sleep alreet?"

"They've all slept that well they haven't emerged yet!" said Andreas.

"Ah thought y'd appreciate a jug o' milk. Just leave it at t'farmhouse door when ye goes. We'll not be 'ere, I'm away t'day."

"Thank you. How much do we owe you?" asked Andreas.

"I'm not chargin' thee lad! Ye can 'ave t'milk. We've a house cow and we've plenty like. Hope ye all 'ave a safe journey. Tek care in this weather. You've a fair trek over't moors ahead of ye, whichever direction yer takin'."

Andreas thanked the farmer for both the milk and for allowing them to camp on her paddock. He assured her there would be no evidence left behind of their presence and they went their separate ways, eager to avoid the rain that was picking up in intensity again.

One by one, the walkers emerged, all stiff and tired and all seriously put out by the deteriorating weather.

"Are you sure we're safe to do this today?" asked Jeremy.

A chorus of: "Yes, we are OK to do this today," and: "We're not just going to sit about here all day are we?" convinced Jeremy that if he stayed, he'd be the only one.

The small shed was used again to make breakfast. Apart from boiling water for the now routine mug of tea, today saw the preparation of bacon butties, which were eaten after some very creamy bowls of cereal had been consumed: creamy, courtesy of the unadulterated, fresh cow's milk given to the hikers by the lady farmer. Joe was especially grateful for the milk as he recognised that this farming family was not particularly well-off and were obviously finding it tough. In Joe's words, the feel of the farm was one of 'financial hardship' and, as Joe had a similar background, no one was going to argue with his diagnosis.

"Notice how, even though she was obviously poor, she still shared her milk and let us camp on her land for free. Some people are just wonderful aren't they? I hope somebody said thank you?" Joe asked.

Andreas assured him she had been thanked, so Joe, at least, was at peace with his morning.

Robert, on the other hand, was getting worried. He pulled Andrew to one side.

"It's not exactly an easy day today," he said, indicating the long moorland walk ahead of them. "If the weather stays like this, it's another day without a view and again we have the potential to get lost in the mist. Let's just hope the track is well marked."

But Andrew wasn't concentrating. Something rather disturbing had happened in the last fifteen minutes that needed sorting out and was inconvenient and rather disgusting to contemplate! He'd used the trowel in a quiet corner of a paddock over the wall. After completing the task in hand, he had buried the 'debris', re-clad himself in the copious layers of clothing necessary to survive a wet day, including hard-to-put-on wet-weather trousers, and then leaped back over the wall. Unfortunately, Andrew's stomach wasn't at all settled and much to his disgust he – cutting a distasteful and painful story short – produced some unexpected extra debris into the back of his bum cheeks! This 'material' was now continually making its presence felt and yet he couldn't be bothered to undo all those layers of clothing to tackle the problem. Surely the discomfort would dissipate? Surely it was something he could ignore? Only time would tell and so he continued preparations to leave without actually getting to grips with the problem – as it were!

In the background, a well-rehearsed clean-up of pots and pans was taking place using the last of the water, soon to be restocked at the farmhouse tap. Tents were folded and bags packed. In no time at all, the hikers – clad in wet-weather gear – were lifting rucksacks on to tired shoulders. At last, an orderly departure was conducted, with Andrew yet again bringing up the rear after checking the corner of the field for litter.

Instead of climbing back up and on to Hasty Bank, the hikers followed the farm road down and around the ridge. This track led on to the B1257 and just a few yards down the hill, towards the Clay Bank viewpoint, appeared the familiar Cleveland Way signs pointing both east and west from the main road.

"Not another climb please, not this early!" complained Jeremy, but in truth felt by everyone. A steep track disappeared into the mist in front of them and, at an alarmingly slow pace, the group began the ascent. Andreas glanced behind and noticed Andrew walking strangely, sort of swinging his backside around and grimacing.

"What's up with you, Andrew? You practising to dance with Orang-utan again!"

"No, I'm fine, 'Dreas. Just a bit of discomfort: I'll be right eventually," was all Andrew could think to say. Andreas ignored him and walked on.

Around them were the ubiquitous sheep and, of course, meadow pipits. The latter seemed in unusually high number, many displaying distress at the presence of the walkers. Despite the weather, the ground nesting meadow pipits were obviously either building their nests, or already incubating eggs.

Yet again, the walkers had the moors to themselves, although to be fair, in the mist it was hard to see if other people were in the vicinity. Today wasn't as windy, so between showers it was possible to hold a conversation with at least immediate neighbours. On top of Round Hill the conversation at the rear of the column swung to frogs, as in puddles next to the track could be seen large clumps of frogspawn.

"I'm amazed they're up here," said Chris. "I mean, it's bitterly cold and it's bleak, open moorland. I just didn't know they existed in places like this."

To one side of the track appeared a beautiful wading bird with plates of golden plumage etched with black-lined borders. Andrew immediately recognised it as a golden plover, even though he had never seen one in summer breeding plumage before.

"We get these in the 'Vale' in quite big flocks in the winter but they look drab. Only in the breeding season do they look as good as this!" Andrew added, pleased at how everyone suddenly seemed more interested in his beloved birds. Golden plovers weren't, however, able to stop Andrew's rear-end discomfort. Next to comment on his obvious difficulties was Chris who asked, with a look of genuine concern, if things were OK!

"Andrew, are you practising for the Ministry of Silly Walks or something?" Chris asked, with reference to the recently screened comedy sketch of the same name from *Monty Python's Flying Circus*.

Either Andrew was distracted by his problems, or maybe he was displaying his frequent gullible lack of judgement, but for whatever reason, telling Chris why he was walking oddly was a massive mistake. Frankly, after the Martin and Janet fiasco, and after witnessing the remorseless ridiculing of Andreas over his 'aircrew' mates and socks, telling Chris he had a lump of wet poo between his buttocks was at least dopey and at very best, stupid. The look of concern so recently displayed on Chris's face was immediately replaced with one of 'thank you, God, for giving me this wonderful gem of knowledge!' Almost immediately he announced the 'juicy morsel' to the rest of the walkers, who found it both hilarious and disgusting. Interestingly though, on this occasion, Andrew was not unduly concerned. Instead, he played up to the humour of the event and exploited the obvious disgust being exhibited by continually reminding everyone of his problem and the gruesome cause. Interestingly, nobody suggested stopping, disrobing and taking time to clean up because, frankly, the weather conditions were atrocious. Periodically, sheets of rain lashed the seven hikers, almost as if a garden hose was being discharged at them full blast. In weather like this the only course of action was to bend the head and concentrate on following the man in front. Step after squishy step after squishy step. Onwards and onwards they trudged, spitting rivulets of water out of their mouths and shaking their heads to clear water from any hair protruding out of fitted hoods.

Between the showers, Martin, Jeremy and Joe would attempt to lead off in song. Apart from more renditions of 'The Happy Wanderer', which incidentally seemed ironic as conditions were so challenging, the singers also tried 'Wandering Star' by Lee Marvin and one or two meaningful songs by Cat Stevens. Even catchy music hall songs such as 'Daisy Bell', 'Roll Out the Barrel' and, of course, 'Down at the Old Bull and Bush' were attempted.

When you consider the love of contemporary music displayed by most of the walkers, it was interesting to note that when actually singing songs along a walking track in the rain, the ones that seemed easiest to sing were the antique tunes. These old songs were learned in passing by the group while their parents were hogging the TV screens and watching *The Good Old Days* broadcast by the BBC from the Leeds City Varieties. Usually aired on a Sunday night, the tunes were generally disliked by teenagers of the era, not because of the age or tempo of the songs, but because they were broadcast the night before school. Somehow, jaunty characters doing 'The Lambeth Walk' signified the turning point between forgetting homework and study and then remembering the same – and what was coming up on Monday morning!

Certainly for Joseph and Jeremy, the fad of glam rock had been a fascination since 1970. Pinpointing glam rock's inception proved difficult, but they agreed it was maybe the T.Rex single 'Ride a White Swan'. Even the hippie band behind the movement shortened their name to announce the change from Tyrannosaurus Rex to T.Rex. For Joe, the words 'Our lives are merely trees of possibilities,' from the song 'Dragon's Ear' by

Tyrannosaurus Rex was about as meaningful and profound as it was possible to get in 1974. Mind you, Joe would have been the first to admit that trying to keep spirits up while walking in the rain on the moors needed something more toe-tapping than that!

Suddenly, the walkers found themselves bunching up. Robert had stopped. As the one leading from the front with the map, he had reached a point of indecision. A huddle of hikers encircled him, the last one to join being Andrew, who was still milking humour from his unmentionable mishap.

"Move over, fellas, I need room to squirm!" he announced as he pushed into the group.

"Will you belt up about your sodding poo issues, please? I don't want to be reminded, just shut it, Andy, and put up with it – we don't need to know!" Jeremy forcibly announced.

A chorus of: "Yeah, shut up about it, Andy, you're making us feel ill," echoed around the group.

Robert looked at Andrew and simply said: "Put a cork in it, Andrew!"

"There's no room for a cork, Rob, the space is already filled mate!" was Andrew's quick reply, which elicited another vocal round of disapproval and Robert's admonishment pointing out that the cork was obviously meant for his mouth.

Robert then described the dilemma he was facing. On the map, the walk turns through forty-five degrees and heads north somewhere on Greenhow Moor. Thanks to the misty conditions, it was hard to know where exactly to make the turn and there were several possibilities. Right next to them was one such choice, which was confusing Robert. However, with a gathering of brains, comparing track direction to compass direction, it was decided this was not the route to take. Had they done so they would have descended through a plantation and ended up on the lowlands in a village called Ingleby Greenhow.

Things got complicated again as the group descended into a dip of wet, swampy ground. Again the map was consulted and the decision taken to continue south-east, despite great temptation to turn north-west. The choice was the correct one and soon the hikers emerged on to the track bed of the old Rosedale Ironstone Railway.

Considering the thick mist, rain and discomfort, the walkers had done well to locate this important crossroads. At this point the Lyke Wake walk and the Coast to Coast walk – the latter only described recently by Wainwright in his book *A Coast to Coast Walk* published in 1973 – branched off in opposite directions to the Cleveland Way. The walkers got a new burst of energy as the abrupt change in direction meant that, for the first time that day, they were heading straight for their ultimate destination – Great Ayton. With purposeful step and dogged determination, the band of hikers continued alongside the railway track towards Tidy Brown Hill. Unseen by the walkers was the view. If the rain had cleared and the mist lifted, the views north and east would have been spectacular. But it wasn't to be and for yet another day the hikers walked in a misty world of their own, again without meeting anyone.

Springing from the heather, a red grouse caused minor consternation. With its distinctive 'ge-back, ge-back, ge-back' call, a beautiful big grouse blasted off right beside Martin and Joe. Martin turned to Andrew with a smile and said.

"Bloody hell, Andrew, what was that?" He then felt his left buttock before announcing, with obvious sarcasm. "With a fright like that it's a wonder I'm not in the same state as you!"

Naturally, Andrew was able to provide an answer. "That was a red grouse, Mart. They feed on young heather shoots, that's why there's burnt patches of heather everywhere. This whole place is managed for sheep and grouse shooting!"

"You mean they shoot sheep up here as well as grouse!" Jeremy added in his usual quick-witted form.

"No, of course not! I meant they put sheep up here to graze the grass, but the grouse eat the heather and they make money running grouse shoots. The Glorious Twelfth they call it: August 12th is when the shooting season starts," Andrew added before pointing to a depression in the ground at the side of the track that was lined with stones. "See, that's a shooting butt. The shooters stand in them pits and the beaters in the distance drive the grouse past them to be shot at."

Jeremy turned up his nose. "Sounds a bit cruel to me and a bit unnecessary, truth be told."

"It's just a way of using the land! It's no different to farming poultry really. It's just they're shot rather than slaughtered in a factory. Don't you eat chicken, Jez?"

"It is different, Andrew. We have to eat, so we have to breed and slaughter chickens. This is a bit sick 'cos the folks doing this are killing for pleasure. For some reason, I reckon killing anything for pleasure is a bit weird and cruel."

Andrew agreed with him. "You are right there, Jez. Trouble is, the hunting and shooting types own woodlands and wildlife habitat that would disappear if they weren't keeping it intact for their sport! For instance, look at all the woodland and 'coverts' around the Vale of Belvoir kept for foxes to live in, just so the hounds have got something to chase. Those woods would be long gone if the hunts didn't exist. I'll tell you what is bad though, all these grouse are looked after by gamekeepers. They consider things such as hen harriers and merlins as vermin and shoot them. That's what I find depressing – all the birds of prey being persecuted."

Chris joined the debate. "Basically, this landscape isn't natural at all. If it weren't for humans managing it for grouse and sheep it would be a stunted birch forest. It's all very well wanting the keepers to leave birds of prey alone, but just imagine all the species that got displaced when we replaced forest with heather moors. I bet there were wolves and bears and such like wandering around back then."

From the front, Joe, Martin and Jeremy could then be heard singing the Dave Edmunds song 'I Hear you Knocking', which proved a useful distraction and lasted until the next belt of rain swept past. The track past Tidy Brown Hill was like all the others the group had walked on, except without excessive undulation. It was only the same, of course, thanks to a complete lack of visibility. The views that should have been blowing the minds of the walkers were yet again hidden from sight. Despite this, the day was unique for its apparent isolation. The walkers couldn't see Teesside with all its industry off to the north, or indeed the villages and farmland immediately beneath the hills. To the seven adventurers, they were in another world: a planet of swirling mist and intermittent rain, in a landscape with no signs of habitation by members of their own species.

Amazingly, there was total faith in Robert's map-reading abilities. Admittedly, now and again there appeared the odd Cleveland Way sign or acorn marker, just to reinforce Robert's direction finding. Unbeknown to the six walkers not carrying a fancy map case, he did have the odd moment of crisis! The odd moment where he guided the group into territory he wasn't totally sure about. Some of the signs and markers on the route gave Robert great relief by their appearance, not that he was about to admit that to everyone else!

At the eastern end of Battersby Moor the route turned north

on to a small country road to begin its descent towards Kildale. This point is where pain really began to show itself. Joseph was in pain because of his shoulders and low-slung pack. Jeremy and Martin both had aching feet and everyone suffered leg and back ache as they walked downhill towards the village. Andrew was struggling with his backpack as one of the shoulder straps kept going slack, which threw the load out of balance. The little teeth on the clasp seemed not to want to grip the yellow nylon strap, probably thanks to water that was soaking everything. On top of this, of course, was a now well-formed, sausage-shaped object continually being kneaded between his buttocks! Nobody wanted to hear about this anymore and, frankly, one or two began to doubt the existence of the said object, despite Andrew's continual reference to its nagging presence. It said a lot for the silent misery felt at this part of the walk that even the appearance of a pair of wheatears, in among some old quarry workings on the edge of the park above Kildale, failed to get any comment from Andrew. Basically, even he didn't have the reserves of energy to sound enthusiastic about anything, even such a striking new bird.

The seven arrived in Kildale at about three in the afternoon. As yet, no one had said anything about lunch. The group huddled together in the lee of a stone house.

"Let's look at the map please, Rob?" Jeremy asked.

"We've got to go up past Captain Cook's Monument on this hill," said Robert, pointing out the route. "Then we go down to this road before turning west towards Great Ayton." Robert's finger again traced the route, which looked deceptively easy. The rain was still pouring, prompting Joe to suggest they only eat apples and chocolate for lunch so they could keep moving. Having said it, he promptly dropped his rucksack and disappeared behind a hedge to attend to another basic need. When he returned, everyone had removed their packs and so a more substantial lunch was procured. Lumps of cheddar cheese with slices of bread, followed by apples, biscuits, chocolate and Kendal Mint Cake seemed to lift spirits, despite the continuing rain.

"Where are we going to camp tonight?" asked Chris.

Andrew replied with an uncharacteristic lack of enthusiasm, thanks to the weather.

"I really have no idea, and you know what, I'm not all that keen on camping in this bloody awful rain!"

Jeremy didn't take much encouraging to be pessimistic. "Andy's right, it's pretty bad. I'm wet down my back and standing here it's getting cold."

Andreas provided the morale-boosting impetus to keep things on track. "Come on then, packs on. The only way to get warm is to move! Come on, let's march fellas! Come on!"

There were odd times when Andreas's bit of 'military' training came to the fore. Getting up and at it in the morning was one example and keeping up morale at times of hardship was another. Of course, Chris would have added purchasing snug fitting socks to this list!

The walk from Kildale under the railway line and uphill towards Bankside Farm was conducted in silence. Walking up the steep hill brought out the worst in the seven walkers. Worst in the form of bad language, aimed directly at Andrew for ever suggesting they undertake the Cleveland Way! The weather was lousy, the hikers were heavily laden and the hill they were climbing was extraordinarily steep. Everyone agreed that whoever the farmers were that lived at Bankside Farm they must be incredibly fit, just through walking up and down their own farmyard!

It was a blessed relief to turn left off the road and on to the forestry track between Mill Bank Wood and Coate Moor. It was even more of a relief to find themselves walking along a fairly level track that was soft underfoot. Another layer of relief suddenly presented itself as the clouds thinned, the rain eased and a watery sun briefly appeared.

Andreas greeted the sunlight with another TV quote. "Shine, tiny sun!" he exclaimed, prompting Martin to ask him which programme that had come from.

"*Catweazle*! You know, the medieval wizard who's been magically brought forward to today! It's a kids' programme really, but it's a good idea!" Andreas answered.

"I've got a quote from a kids' book! It's one we used to read as kids all the time and it's got stuck in my brain. It's from *Rupert Bear*! Listen to this, it's brilliant!" announced Martin, before astounding the walkers with a memorable Rupert rhyme from his childhood:

"And Golly stared! And Rupert stared and Uncle Tom stared He.
For on the watch chain by the door there hung the magic key!

"What do you reckon to that bit of poetic genius?" Martin added with a beaming smile, knowing only too well he had presented something incredibly childish. The amazing thing was, he had emphasised the phrases so well and delivered the lines in such an animated fashion, that they had come across as quite thrilling!

"I've got a poem for you that I wrote myself called 'Why do you love me, Lord?'" said Joe, who went on to deliver his own moving creation, one that even Andrew had to admit asked a lot of meaningful questions.

Joe recited loudly to the group:
"Why do you love me, Lord?
What did I do?
Why aren't I dying in Africa, too?

Why do you love me, Lord?
Why excuse me?
Why aren't I in prison never to be free?

People are dying of disease and of cold
Why should I live until I am old?

Why do you love me, Lord?
While other's cry.
I am still living,
Whilst millions must die.

"Well, what do you reckon? I wrote that one myself!"

An appreciative chorus of "well done, Joe" and "good on ya, Joe" went up from the group, including the atheists!

"You want some Alfred Lord Tennyson?" Andrew asked. Interestingly, poetry was the least likely subject to enthral Andrew and yet his contribution to this debate was to prove fairly sophisticated. The fact he had remembered it was entirely due to its ornithological content. The first time he read it, during an English class a couple of years earlier, he had been instantly thrilled, to the extent his hair stood up on the back of his neck as the words hit home. The poem was simply entitled *The Eagle* and, because it was relatively short, Andrew was able to recite it quite easily:

"He clasps the crag with crooked hands
Close to the sun in lonely lands
Ring'd with the azure world he stands.

The wrinkled sea beneath him crawls
He watches from his mountain walls
And like a thunderbolt he falls!

"What do reckon to that then?" Andrew asked triumphantly.

"Not bad from a bloke that all day has been full of shit!" added Andreas, who then went on to completely lower the tone by reciting the limerick currently written on the wall in the upper school lavatories:

"There was a young fellow called Dave,
Who kept a dead whore in a cave.
He said I'll admit I'm a bit of a shit,
But think of the money I'll save!"

This brought a round of laughter from most of the group and a snort of disgust from Joseph. At this point, the group clambered across a small wall and out into an open field with the huge monolith of Captain Cook's Monument in front of them. The top of this impressive needle had been emerging through the mist for several minutes, but only as they approached was the full scale and majesty of this memorial revealed.

For the first time that day, the walkers shared the space with other people. An elderly couple were examining the plaque on the far side of the spire dressed in clear plastic waterproofs. She wore a red head scarf and he a flat cap. Running alongside them was a small Yorkshire terrier wearing a tartan dog coat. They expressed surprise at seeing the group emerge from the mist.

"What are you lads then? Are you on army exercise or something?" The elderly gentleman enquired.

"I don't think the army would wander round reciting stuff from *Rupert Bear*!" said Robert sarcastically, before explaining politely the reason for his comment and for the group's temporary presence at the monument. He went on to ask the couple where they were from.

"We're from Hartlepool, just the other side of Middlesbrough. You know, near Sunderland and Newcastle."

All this was said in a broad Geordie accent that fascinated everyone present. Jeremy was all ears because all the places mentioned were homes to some of England's best football teams.

"Aye, we're very lucky living where we are. To the north is Northumberland with its beaches and beautiful countryside and to the south we've got the North York Moors National Park. We often go for day trips like today. You know, to see interesting places."

Jeremy decided he would go for one of his 'last laughs': "You're right!" he added with gusto. "Actually, I'd consider living round here myself if you had some decent football teams!"

This brought laughter from the walkers and even from the elderly couple, who were essentially the butt of Jeremy's sledgehammer wit. After bidding farewell, the walkers began another painful descent across Little Ayton Moor down to Dikes Lane. Once on the road, the rain started yet again. Robert indicated a left-hand turn off the Cleveland Way and down the road towards Great Ayton, still with no idea where the walkers would end up staying the night.

The walk to Great Ayton was like adding insult to injury. The distance was just great enough to feel wrong. They walked past the little railway station and continued along Station Road towards the town. Everyone was exhausted and so walking a route that wasn't actually part of the Cleveland Way seemed to go against the grain. The old saying 'it could be worse, it could be raining,' didn't apply because it was 'precipitating' it down! Not only that, it was getting dark early. The sky was dank, the air cold and they were late. To make matters worse, they were hungry and Andrew still had a lump of poo bouncing around in his undies!

"We're not camping! Please tell me we're not camping!" cried out an exhausted and frustrated Jeremy.

"What the hell else can we do, Jez?" asked Joe. "I don't want to camp any more than you do, but I can't afford a hotel or anything!"

At this point, the hikers began to enter the outskirts of Great Ayton. Robert was in the lead and so was first to meet an oncoming pedestrian. He enquired as to the whereabouts of a campsite and was somewhat alarmed to be told there were none. When the gentleman had walked on, the hikers gathered round to contemplate the fact there was nowhere to camp.

"We need a site with toilets and showers tonight, but that chap says there isn't one in Great Ayton!" Robert informed the group.

"He mightn't know!" commented Andrew. "Let's ask a policeman if we can have a cell or something?"

This casual remark seemed to go down well with the group, who decided there and then that sleeping in a police cell would be preferable to sleeping in the great outdoors, at least for tonight. Further enquiry located the police station and the seven walkers seemed to find renewed vigour at the prospect of some police hospitality!

All seven pushed their way into a small atrium in the front

of the police station. The air was warm and the faint smell of coffee and some form of cooked food greeted the hikers. A red-faced sergeant swivelled round in his swivel chair and gave the assembled mob the once over.

"What are ye lot then? Refugees? Illegal immigrants? Or are we at war an' naybodies telling me?" The fact he was smiling belied any fear the hikers may have had at confronting such an outspoken member of the police force.

"We're from Leicestershire and... " at this point Robert was cut off by the sergeant.

"So it's an invasion then, lad, is it?" the sergeant wittily interrupted.

With a smile Robert continued. "Well, not quite an invasion, more an embarrassment. You see we're walking the Cleveland Way and we're somewhat wet and we've just found out there's no campsite in Great Ayton and, to cut a long story short, we wondered if we might be allowed to spend a night in the cells?"

"Bloody hell, I've heard it all now! Over t'years we've 'ad plenty stay in t'cells overnight, but I can honestly say naybodies ever voluntarily asked to be there! Unbelievable!"

Andrew decided to add his thoughts. "Well, we can't afford hotels, or anything, so we're sort of desperate really. Frankly we don't know what to do?"

The policeman stood up and approached the counter. "Well, I'm sorry, lads, but we can't possibly put ye up in a police cell an' that's final. Ye're reet, we don't have a campsite as such in Great Ayton, but ye all look as if ye needs a bit of shelter. Ye all look fagged out! Now listen. Across t'way there's the vicar, the Reverend Appleyard. He's a really nice fella, ye'll all get on wi' 'im I'm sure. He's let youngsters like yerselves sleep in 'is garage before. I'll give 'im a ring and see what I can fix up!"

A round of "thank yous" emanated from the hikers as they stood dripping in the police station entrance. After a short discussion on the phone, the policeman returned to the walkers. "Good news, lads, the vicar seys he'll let ye sleep in t'garage! The vicarage is around to the right. Just across t'road there's t'church. Go through t' yard and ye'll see the gates leading to t'vicarage. Then go up to the house and knock on t'door, that's if he's not already outside waitin' for ye all!"

After another heartfelt round of "thank yous" aimed at the constabulary and a genuine "good luck for t' rest of t' walk" expressed by the policeman, the explorers found themselves walking across the road heading for the vicarage. Joseph was at the front with Robert to broker negotiations with the vicar. It seemed a good idea to have a devout believer conducting contractual obligations with one of God's earthbound representatives!

They found the entranceway to the vicarage and walked the short distance across the grass to the front door. Before they could knock, however, a voice from the left called them across towards some trees and bushes in front of a nice new garage. The roller door on the garage was retracted into the ceiling and standing, illuminated in saint-like majesty inside the building, was a splendid country vicar, complete with black shirt and pullover and, of course, a white dog collar.

"Good evening, lads, and welcome to sunny Great Ayton! I've been praying for sunshine, but for some reason my mate upstairs isn't listening. I suppose he's getting organised for Good Friday tomorrow, just like I am!" the Reverend Appleyard announced.

Joe took over as spokesman and almost prostrated himself giving thanks for the kind offer of the garage to sleep in. He apologised for interrupting the vicar's Good Friday sermon preparations and assured him the hikers wouldn't make a mess or damage the vicar's property. In turn, the vicar pointed to some bushes next to the garage and suggested they be used for urinating behind, but anything more would need a visit to the public loos, which were in the town centre. The vicar also gave directions to the nearest chip shop, which thankfully meant no cooking was necessary. Ominously, though, he did warn the campers that his son normally parked in the garage and that he should be home later that night or in the early hours.

"Don't worry, he's bound to notice you in the headlights after he's lifted the roller door. Keep your comings and goings quiet so as not to disturb anyone and we'll see you in the morning. There's a water tap round the side that has drinkable water, so feel free to use that as well. Good night lads, and God bless!" With that the vicar walked back to his home, leaving seven young men from Leicestershire in temporary charge of his nice new garage.

The very first thing that happened was the blessed relief of putting down their rucksacks. Taking them off for the night was a marvellous sensation and walking without them seemed so much easier.

Joe was determined to get some food before settling down for the night. "Come on fellas, let's go and get fish and chips before taking all the wet-weather gear off. I mean it's still raining, so whatever happens, we will need to keep wearing the stuff."

Before leaving, everyone unpacked sleeping bags and laid them out in the garage to air. Some damp clothes were also spread round the room. Then it was back into the street, only this time free of the heavy rucksacks they had carried all day. Fortunately, the fish and chip shop was open so an easy evening meal was had.

On the way back, the rain began to ease, although it was still cold. Once inside the garage removal of wet clothing became top priority. It wasn't long before rafters, chairs and a workbench were all festooned with waterproof clothing, together with various shirts and trousers. One or two of the hikers cleaned their teeth just outside the garage and most took advantage of the bushes.

Meanwhile, in the back corner, Andrew was attending to a problem that had plagued him all day. Down to his underwear, Andrew was well able, with the help of some toilet tissue, to remove a uniquely shaped and hairy 'object' from between his buttocks! Not wishing to deprive the evening of some self-deprecating humour he held the said 'object' aloft and said out loud: "See, told you I had a problem. Look what I've done!"

For some reason, everybody looked over. For obvious reasons, everyone was horrified and totally disgusted. All efforts aimed at noise reduction were abandoned. All deference to the ecclesiastical surrounds thrown out of the window as the remaining six walkers let Andrew know in no uncertain terms what he should do with the said 'object'. Quite an ironic response really, when you consider that was exactly where the 'object' had just come from!

Chapter 11

Great Ayton to Skelton

Despite the fact sleeping bags were spread on a solid concrete floor in the vicar's garage, sleep had come easily to most of the explorers. The one exception was Robert, who for some reason couldn't stop thinking that at some point the vicar's son was due to arrive home, leaving him feeling vulnerable. Suppose he didn't notice the sleeping hikers after he lifted the roller door? What a terrible accident it would be if a car ploughed into them. So, as he was still awake, Robert was the one who greeted the well-dressed young man who – at one thirty in the morning – lifted the roller door.

"Bloody hell, how many of you are there?" The vicar's son exclaimed as his headlights illuminated the seven bulging sleeping bags on the floor of a garage festooned with damp, musty clothing. It should be noted at this point that the walkers themselves did not notice, or even consider themselves, 'musty' – but other people did! Had any of the seven been able to read body language, they would have noticed the policeman earlier turn up his nostrils when the hikers entered his police station. This alone should have been sign enough that they were, ever so slightly, on the nose. Had anyone noticed the vicar's son nearly lose his breath when he opened the door, as a wave of warm musty stench hit him full in the face, then they would have been under no illusion that they were a tad smelly! But ignorance is bliss and as each smelt as bad as his neighbour, no one was aware of just how antisocial the group was becoming. While sleeping in an out of the way vicar's garage it didn't matter so much, and walking on the Yorkshire Moors it didn't matter at all. However, unbeknown to the walkers, a problem was building that would plague them for the rest of the Cleveland Way. Well not necessarily plague them, but plague anyone who interacted with them from this point on!

Robert answered the late returning vicar's son. "There's seven of us and your dad has kindly let us sleep here for the night. He warned us you would be back later. We're walking the Cleveland Way and kinda got caught out by the weather, I'm sorry that you'll have to leave your car out in the rain. Hope you don't mind too much?"

"No, that's all right! Believe it or not this has happened before, but not with quite so many people crammed in there. I'll park up and leave you alone! Goodnight." With that he rolled the door back down and left the now semi-awake walkers, who in their sleeping bags looked like a herd of walruses hauled up on a beach, to get off to sleep.

At daybreak, Andreas was first to get out of his sleeping bag. He was later than he and the rest of the group had wanted to be, only emerging at eight thirty in the morning. Straightaway he hauled the roller door up and a welcome blast of fresh air greeted the dozing campers.

"Come on, fellas, let's get at it. We're later than we should be! Good news though, it's not raining. Come on, another day beckons," said an overexcited Andreas to a groggy and unenthusiastic garage full of explorers.

Wearily, with aching limbs and bodies still craving sleep, everyone emerged into the new day. Slowly, but surely, the process of getting dressed and packed began. Breakfast was a hurried affair as it was decided a visit to the public loos was necessary, sooner rather than later. A bigger than usual lunch break was planned for later on, one that included frying sausages. As they were packing, the Reverend Appleyard paid the garage a visit.

"Did you sleep all right, boys? I can see my son's car parked in the drive, so he found you then!"

Joseph took over as spokesman and made all the necessary 'thank yous'. During the pack up, it was decided that Jeremy should make a one pound donation to the church, which he duly did from the reserves held in the kitty.

Leaving the vicar to psyche himself for his Good Friday sermons, the seven made for the brick public toilet block in town. On locating the loos, it was painfully obvious there weren't enough cubicles in the men's section to cope with the demand. There was only the urinal and one cubicle. Andrew, in particular, was inconvenienced and decided, as no one else was around, to utilise the ladies' lavatories. The opportunity for humour was not lost on those stood outside. After a few minutes, Jeremy whispered loudly: "Watch out, Andy, there's a lady heading this way."

"Thanks, Jez!" A somewhat stressed Andrew replied from behind the closed door of his cubicle.

At this point, Robert walked into the ladies and without saying a word attended to his ablutions in the next cubicle to Andrew, who was, of course, of the opinion he was sharing the ladies' loos with a female from Great Ayton. Andrew sat quietly while the 'lady' in the next stall conducted her 'business' in a manner Andrew found most educational. Until this point, Andrew had assumed the fairer sex would attend to such matters in a gentile, quiet and refined fashion. The noises from the 'lady' were anything but ladylike. Only when Robert attempted to ask Andrew to push paper under the dividing wall, because there wasn't any next door, did Andrew twig he had been had. This was despite Robert's attempt to imitate a female voice!

As the laughter was dying down, Jeremy could again be heard whispering loudly. "Fellas! Watch it, there's a lady coming in!"

Now here was a dilemma for both Robert and Andrew. There were only two cubicles in the ladies' lavatory and they were occupying both. Neither could be absolutely certain that Jeremy was telling the truth. On the other hand, if he was telling the truth, how were they going to get out of this one! Robert summed up the situation with one whispered word. "Shit!"

Andrew quickly, in a female voice, whispered back, "If only I could! Thanks to you and Jeremy I've been sat here too frightened and scared to do anything. You'll have to go out! I need to stay!"

At this point the unmistakeable footsteps of a woman could be heard walking into the toilets. They stopped. Andrew and Robert stopped and stared at the closed doors of their cubicles. Silence reigned for too long.

A woman's voice, with tones of embarrassment, asked. "Will you be long?"

Andrew decided to cement his position in Great Ayton's public lavatory by quickly replying in his best 'female voice'. "Yes, sorry!"

Robert followed suit with a simple apology, this time with a more convincing female intonation in his voice. "Sorry!"

The lady could be heard turning and walking out. Robert waited a while before flushing the toilet, nervously washing his hands, and rejoining the others. Andrew followed soon after.

"We didn't know what to do when she walked in there!"

said Jeremy, with a beaming smile. "It was all we could do not to start laughing!"

"She gave us a funny look when she walked away though," commented Joe. "I reckon she figured out what was going on. Mind you, it was really funny. I wouldn't have missed it for the world!"

The seven walkers then bade farewell to Great Ayton and headed up the road past the station, through a narrow gap between houses on Dikes Lane and onward to the car park below Captain Cook's Monument. At this point, the walkers picked up the Cleveland Way again and began to head north.

Jeremy articulated everybody's thoughts. "We're starting uphill early today, aren't we? It couldn't just start flat, could it? My legs are killing me and we've hardly started!"

Again, everyone was thinking just the same, but the effort of actually saying it was too much trouble. Besides, it made no difference as the track went uphill and that was that! After a short steep climb the track levelled off beside a stone wall, which guided the walkers alongside Great Ayton Moor. The day was misty, but the view down to farmland in the valley below and across to the 'Teesside Matterhorn' of Roseberry Topping in the north-west, was not totally obscured. The Cleveland Way then turns sharply eastward, that is once Roseberry Topping has been conquered!

At this point, a major disagreement broke out between Andrew and the rest of the team.

"It says in the book we should climb Roseberry Topping. Then we return here and carry on the walk," said Andrew, concerned that by not doing this diversion it would somehow disqualify them from claiming to have walked the entire Cleveland Way. None of the others were very keen. Martin seemed most likely to be swayed.

"Come on, Mart, you'll do it with me, won't you? Don't let me be the only one who, at the end of the day, can honestly say he's walked the entire Cleveland Way!"

Chris commented. "No one will know if you don't tell 'em, Andy!"

Joe added: "Just 'cos it's written in the book doesn't mean you have to do it, Andrew!"

Andrew wasn't happy and vented his growing frustration on Joe. "You're a fine one to talk about following the written word, Joe! I mean, that's what you base your life on isn't it, when you follow everything written in the Bible?"

"None of us are going, Andrew. Instead, we're going to sit and cook sausages and have a nice restful lunch! If you want to climb it, you can. We'll just look after your rucksack."

After attempting to plead with Martin and Andreas, Andrew gave up. He dropped his backpack against the wall and took off down the hill in the direction of Roseberry Topping. The other six took out the stoves and proceeded to fry sausages and berate Andrew Price for being such a complete pain in the proverbial. Unfortunately, they couldn't put his exploits out of their minds as the view across the valley and up the track to the top of Roseberry Topping was clearly visible and the running figure of Andrew was in full view the whole way! When Andrew reached the top he was roughly at the same height as the sausage cookers and could be seen waving to them from the pinnacle as they tucked in. In a united show of defiance, or possibly annoyance, no one bothered to wave back!

Jeremy was quick to point out something disturbing. "He's never going to let us forget this is he! For the rest of our lives, if we ever meet up with the prick, he's going to rub it in that he was the only one to have really walked the Cleveland Way!"

Chris agreed, but expressed some admiration. "You're right, Jez, he's going to be more painful than ever. But you've got to admit, he's bloody fit to run down that slope and then up that hill to the summit, especially after all the walking we've done lately!"

Robert had the final say: "He's fit all right and he can be a pain in the backside! Mind you, it's a shame all the sausages will be gone by the time he gets back!"

With that, the six members of the expedition left waiting on Newton Moor proceeded to eat a fulfilling lunch, including half a chocolate bar that 'leapt' out at them from one of the side pockets in Andrew's rucksack!

There was no mercy shown. As Andrew ran back up the rise to rejoin the walkers his six colleagues were already kitted up and prepared to start back along the Cleveland Way. After 'thanking' his 'friends' for saving him a sausage, a comment that earned him a sincere "you're welcome" from the six replete members of the team, Andrew put on his rucksack, and, forgoing lunch, scrambled after them. Mind you, he gave as good as he got by being at pains to describe the magnificent views from Roseberry Topping at every opportunity. Whenever the walkers stopped to admire a view, during those rare moments when the mist lifted, Andrew would always add the proviso that: "It's not as good as the view from Roseberry Topping! But, of course, since you haven't walked the proper Cleveland Way route you obviously wouldn't know!"

The walk settled into a steady pace across Hutton Moor and down into a valley with moorland on one side and grassland on another. While passing Highcliffe Farm, the rain began again. As the track turned towards Highcliffe Nab the already restricted view became even more blanketed by mist. Amongst some spindly trees the walkers reluctantly put on their wet-weather gear, Joe leading a toilet break yet again before wrapping himself in waterproof clothing.

On top of Highcliff Nab, in between bursts of rain, the outskirts of Guisborough shifted from visible to obscured. The walk through Guisborough Woods was damp and at times difficult. At one point, Robert made a mistake that resulted in the walkers going downhill and emerging on a track next to fields on Belman Bank. All credit to Robert though, as he had been saying for some minutes that, according to the map, the walkers shouldn't be descending! Only on emerging from the trees did his suspicions become confirmed. Despite complaints from 'the ranks' the problem was resolved by returning to a point in the middle of the forest where the Cleveland Way takes an unusual uphill dog-leg. For some reason, the acorn sign on a wooden post had been misinterpreted by Robert and no one else had noticed the obvious error. Still, it was the first time a navigation mistake had been made, so no one made a big issue of it.

The rain persisted and got worse, making this another silent walk where all the hikers could do was keep putting one foot after another. As the route descended alongside Spa Wood, the sound of motor vehicles could be heard.

Chris asked: "Are we coming to a road, Robert?"

"Yes, we are. The Guisborough to Whitby road is what you can hear. We cross it in a minute and then head towards the coast."

Jeremy said something that again nobody disagreed with. "Don't tell me we're camping in this tonight? Seriously, fellas, the last thing we need to be doing today is sleeping in a tent. Besides, I need a shower!"

"It might be best to take a hotel room, or get bed and breakfast tonight," said Joe, who, due to financial constraints, would only ever say this if he was absolutely desperate to avoid camping.

Joe was also interested in the disturbed landscape they were passing through before reaching the main road. It was left to Andrew to explain that the scarred land around Slapewath was caused by ancient iron ore mining and that just north of here on Teesside was where the world's first industrial smelting of iron had occurred.

Mind you, the disturbed ground gave Joe somewhere to hide for yet another of his toilet breaks.

"Is it just me, or is this like taking a dog for a walk and watching it mark its territory?" suggested Chris, as for the umpteenth time the group waited for Joseph to cock his leg behind another unfortunate tree.

After crossing the Guisborough to Whitby road, the walkers were somewhat horrified to be confronted by a steep track alongside a great circular hole cut into Spring Bank by ancient alum miners. Ordinarily, the walkers would have taken such a climb with a pinch of salt but today they were wet and tired. Yet again, the weather had transpired to deprive them of the reward for a steep climb, which of course was a view. Instead, arriving at the top of Spring Bank simply produced a fog and mist enshrouded world, with the sound of vehicles driving along the main road in the valley below. Still, the walk was in front of them and, apart from a slight muddy climb from Rawcliffe Banks Wood to Airy Hill Lane, it was either level, or only slightly descending.

The rain continued to pour, making Airy Hill Lane take on the appearance of a stream. At one point, a warty toad crossed the road, creating interest for everyone. Finally, out of the mist on the right-hand side of the track, emerged slate-roofed rows of houses.

Robert consulted the map. "This is Skelton Green. We should try and find bed and breakfast, or something!"

Andreas, who was feeling particularly wet and miserable, suggested the seven find a phone box and look for accommodation. Joe agreed and suggested he be allowed to contact Yvonne, but this was deemed, very vociferously, to be a selfish request and was promptly disallowed. Andreas's idea was accepted and a brief diversion off the Cleveland Way into Skelton Green followed. The streets were deserted, which was hardly surprising as, not only was it tea time, but it was a 'filthy' evening. Apart from rain, it was getting colder by the minute, so it was with increasing desperation that the seven walkers searched for a public telephone.

Eventually, a red phone box emerged out of the mist. Andreas dropped his pack and went in, followed by Robert and Andrew. Admittedly, Andrew only partly entered the shelter of the box as there wasn't room. It might have helped if he and Robert had taken off their rucksacks, but neither could be bothered. Andreas was carrying a two pence coin to make a local call. On the wall next to the phone was a series of advertisements for taxi firms, restaurants and one hotel. With an invitation to enjoy comfortable rooms and breakfast complete with 'free parking' was an advert for the Holly Bush Inn. Andreas picked up the receiver and put his two pence into the slot. He dialled the number written on the notice and waited for a reply. A woman answered and he pressed button A, but Andreas had not thought the call through and announced the following to the amazement and amusement of the others:

"Hello, we're cold, tired and depressed and don't feel like pitching in this damned weather!"

Then he waited for a reply, which for obvious reasons didn't come! The poor Holly Bush woman hadn't made head nor tail of his announcement! Robert grabbed the phone from Andreas and explained the predicament the seven walkers were in. Now understanding their circumstances, the woman on the other end went off to consult with her boss. Robert then found himself negotiating with Mr Kelly, the owner of the Holly Bush Inn. After what seemed to be a long and drawn out discussion, he returned the receiver to its cradle and turned, smiling, to the group.

"I reckon I've done all right! We've got two rooms with twin beds in each room, plus breakfast for all seven of us, for ten pound 75 pence all up! Not only that, but each room has its own shower and toilet! Luxury!"

Andreas, who was still feeling piqued about having the phone dragged away from him, was quick to point out the obvious fact that there wasn't an actual bed for everyone.

Robert replied: "Yes, I know that, but it would have cost another fiver. They said they had some single mattresses and would put them on the floor for us, so it's not so bad. What we'll do is draw lots for the beds and the rest can sleep on the floor. Mr Kelly, he's the owner by the way who I've just been speaking to, said that's OK. He sounds really nice and friendly. I honestly think we've struck lucky with the first place we found!"

A sense of relief was felt by all the hikers as the prospect of a night under canvas in rainy weather was daunting to say the least. Andreas asked Robert another obvious question. One he already knew Robert couldn't answer.

"How do we get there then? You did get directions while you were on the phone didn't you? Had I been able to finish talking before being rudely interrupted, I would have asked for directions, so I suppose you know how to get there?!"

Robert was taken aback and just for once lost for words.

Despite his supreme confidence and willingness to take command, he had forgotten to ask directions and just the look on his face answered Andreas's question.

Andreas didn't bother with a lengthy reproach. He just shook his head and used a couple of his television catchphrases, this time from *Dad's Army* and *Laurel and Hardy*.

"You stupid boy!" was all he said, followed by: "Here's another fine mess you've gotten us into!"

Alongside one of the houses, a lone local emerged from a small wooden pigeon loft. He had been tending his beloved racing pigeons and was about to attempt the mad dash to the warmth of his front room. Andreas was quick to ask him a question.

"Excuse me!" he politely said.

"Why, wot ye done, lad?" the pigeon fancier retorted, the weather doing nothing to detract from the well-known humour of the region!

Andreas was taken aback. "Nothing, I've done nothing!"

Chris saw an opportunity for comedic greatness. "What do you mean nothing, 'Dreas! Tell him what you and the Air Training Corps get up to with socks!"

Robert stepped in to restore order. "'Why, what have you done', that's very funny! We're walking the Cleveland Way, but because it's so wet we're going to be staying at the Holly Bush Inn tonight. Could you please tell us how to get there?"

"Aye, lad, jus' foller t'Cleveland Way path on't Skelton high street. Ye can pick t'track up agin at t'bottom of t'street, there's a sign off t'right like, directin' ye 'cross a field, ye can't miss it. Foller t'track to the main street o' Skelton, that's where t'shops are. Turn right away from t'Cleveland Way, along t'main street, till ye get past t'church, then on past t'Wharton Arms pub and tek the next left, Saltburn Lane. Then turn right on Station Road and there's the Holly Bush!" With that he wished the hikers good luck and disappeared indoors.

Just the prospect of a roof over their heads and a shower spurred the walkers on and in no time at all they were at the entrance way to the Holly Bush Inn. The front doors were locked, so the seven bundled their way into the public bar off to the side. Immediately, a worried gentleman rushed from behind the bar to meet the walkers. His first thoughts were of concern for his carpets, given the incredibly dishevelled appearance of the walkers. His second were of regret at having rented two of his beautiful rooms to such a wet and grubby mob of youths!

"Lads, I'm sorry, I'm going to have to ask you to use the fire escape to get to your rooms. You're all too filthy to come in through here!"

Behind the proprietor, propping up the bar, a row of smiling locals were enjoying the diversion. Mr Kelly despatched the barmaid to open the fire escape door from the inside. He then led the hikers outside into the rain and up the steel fire escape steps. As they reached the door, it opened from within and once more the heavily laden walkers found shelter.

"These are your rooms, lads. Please take your boots off before you go inside and please do your best not to get the place too dirty! You're welcome to come down to the bar for a drink, but I'll not serve you too much alcohol as you don't look old enough! Breakfast is downstairs at eight in the morning. There's fish and chip shops in the town. Make yourselves at home and I'll send the barmaid back up with a key for the outside of the fire escape door, so you don't have to come back in through the front door."

With that, he left them to make themselves at home. Robert accepted the fire escape key from the returning barmaid with a smile and a twinkle in his eye and, much to the envy of those who witnessed it, he got a twinkle back!

In the first hour the showers received a major workout. Not only did aching, dirty bodies get washed, but so did socks, undies and shirts. Radiators in the rooms and out in the corridor were festooned with clothing. Rucksacks were lined up around the walls and lots were drawn to decide who had a bed and who slept on the floor. Robert, Martin, Jeremy and Joseph shared one room, with Martin and Joseph sleeping on the floor. In the second room, Chris and Andreas had the beds with Andrew on the floor.

Once showered, and wearing reasonably clean spare clothes, the seven walkers headed back into Skelton for yet another fish and chip supper. As it was Good Friday, the town was particularly quiet with most shops and cafés closed. Joe seemed quite happy to be eating fish again as it was in keeping with his beliefs to eat a fish meal at some stage on Good Friday. The rain had eased, so wet-weather gear was left to air in the rooms. The only things not getting a chance to dry and recover were the boots. Nobody had carried extra footwear, so the boots were in continual use and, as they were now wet and muddy, this became a problem, especially when trying to keep clean in a town environment. However, by stomping in puddles the worst of the mud was removed, making entry to the chip shop more acceptable.

Joseph was keen to get hold of Yvonne and made another attempt to phone. This time there was no answer at all, so he vowed to use the hotel stationery, provided in the room, to write her a letter. As it was Easter, several phone calls were made to family, just assuring them that the walkers were safe, well fed and still making progress. Robert even made a short call to Ruth, although he didn't admit this show of weakness to the group.

Eventually, the seven found themselves sitting in the bar drinking shandy, which was all Mr Kelly would allow. The bar was not crowded and the walkers were able to form a tight circle in one corner of the room.

Jeremy led the conversation. "We must be about halfway surely?"

"Well, it must be around halfway for me at least, but then I went that extra mile by conquering Roseberry Topping!" Andrew announced, knowing full well he would be hitting a raw nerve.

"See, I told you he'd never let up about Roseberry flamin' Topping!" Jeremy said.

"The sausages were really nice, though!" added Martin. Everyone agreed in an attempt to irritate Andrew.

Naturally it failed completely and he continued to tease by yet again describing the superior views to be had from Roseberry Topping and how climbing it was really the high-light of the Cleveland Way. Frankly, it was a not-to-be-missed experience.

"Oh, but sorry, you did miss it, didn't you? Don't worry, I don't mind telling you how good it was up there and obviously when we get home if anyone asks us about the Cleveland Way I can enlighten them fully can't I? Good job I did it really!! At least none of you need worry that the full story of walking the Cleveland Way won't be revealed!"

Andreas told him, in no uncertain terms, to put a sock in it and Chris reinforced this by suggesting he use one of Andreas's Air Training Corp socks. The conversation returned to more sophisticated levels. Martin and Joe started on music again, discussing the works of Paul Simon and Bob Dylan. It began to look as if religion would raise its head again as the discussion returned to Cat Stevens and 'The Wind' from the album

Teaser and the Firecat. Jeremy had other ideas though and steered conversation on to fashion, a subject almost everyone present had an opinion on. Jeremy was keen to get hold of a long, grey military overcoat so he could abandon his parka when 'touring' with the band.

Eventually, the conversation returned to females and, yet again, more names were banded about for silent contemplation or vocal appreciation. Joseph mentioned Rosanna. All the boys knew who seventeen-year-old Rosanna was: blonde, slender, adventurous, humorous and provocative, hated by many of the other girls and admired by boys who loved to live dangerously. Rosanna was ever with friends and never alone. At school, the sixth form common room was strictly a no-go area for teachers. It was regularly filled with smoke and the sounds of the latest rock album.

"Let me tell you about Rosanna and me in the common room at school!" Joseph exclaimed. "Only a few months ago, the glam rockers, including Jeremy, were fighting for the turntable with the opposition, the progressive rockers…"

Jeremy interrupted Joseph to add: "At least our songs only last four minutes, not forty!"

"You're dead right, Jeremy! But Rosanna always gets her way when she squirms to the deck. She puts on Leonard Cohen, which seems to please the intellectuals who like it short and sweet!"

"Don't you mean short and bitter?" commented Martin, with his take on the music of Leonard Cohen.

Joseph continued: "Everything's sweet with Rosanna, Mart! A couple of months ago, before I started going out with Yvonne, I was playing poker in the corner of the common room with Tim Baxter, John Reader and Peter Weston. I had three kings and a couple of fours, my luck was in! Rosanna slithered through the crowd and sat on my knee and just looked in my eyes and smiled. I said: 'Come on, Ros, you're embarrassing me. Can't you see I'm in a game!'"

"Lucky bugga!" said Jeremy. "I'd love her to do that to me!"

Joe continued with his tale. "She looked at me and said: 'It's Rosanna, not Ros. Now say it.' So I thought, she'll sit here forever if I don't say her name properly, so I said it. As I pursed my lips for the first syllable it provoked a kiss full on my lips! Then she whispered: 'Now take me out.' So I said 'all right' and as she got up she shouted to her friends: 'One things for sure girls, he's got a good hand!' I never got chance to take her out 'cos Johnny Colishaw moved quicker than me. Actually, I think he's still taking her out!"

"You mean you missed a chance to take Rosanna Townsend out! That's terrible, Joe!" said Robert, who had long fancied her.

"It's sad all right because, thanks to her, I lost the card game as well, but at least I got a kiss!" Joseph replied.

Chris brought things back to basics by enquiring what was coming up on the rest of the Cleveland Way.

Andrew knew exactly what was coming up. "The scenery is about to change dramatically for us now. Once we get past Saltburn we spend the rest of the walk going alongside the sea. So we've cliffs to contend with, beaches, river valleys and, of course, all the seaside towns like Whitby and Scarborough. It's like starting a whole new walk. Really, this is what makes the Cleveland Way so interesting, you know, the contrast between lonely inland moors and the coastline."

"I suppose there won't be a shortage of campsites on this section. I only hope the weather improves so we can actually see the scenery we're walking through!" Chris added hopefully.

"Well, we've come through the toughest walking on the

Cleveland Way in some pretty bad weather. It can only get better now. Really, when you think about it, we're on the home straight, the run down the coast to Filey," said Andrew, clearly very pleased with both progress and prospects.

Two of the local men, formerly leaning on the bar, came over and addressed the seven hikers. They were about 25, with tattooed, muscular arms and strong Geordie accents.

"We know you're walking the Cleveland Way, Mr Kelly's told us about you. We wondered where you're all from? Your accents are from south of here, we're guessing Midlands somewhere?"

Robert became spokesman. "That's right, we're from the Vale of Belvoir." (Which Robert of course pronounced the correct 'local way', the Vale of Beaver).

"Where the hell's the Vale of Beaver then? Don't tell me you've got beavers living in your rivers down there!"

Joseph, being the historian took over. "Well, we all call it the Vale of Beaver, but it's spelt B.E.L.V.O.I.R., which is French for beautiful view. But the locals, years ago, didn't like the French much and to avoid using a French word started calling it beaver!"

"Nobody's going to argue with that logic are they, not even today?" one of the locals replied with a smile. "And what is the Vale of Belvoir famous for then, apart from poncy French names?"

Martin was next to contribute to the debate. "Stilton cheese, Melton Mowbray pork pies and fox hunting! That's about it really. What about you lot round here?"

"We've got all the heavy industry like steel making, ship-building and chemical factories over in Teesside. If you're walking the Cleveland Way you've probably seen it all from the hills?"

Martin again was quick to add his thoughts. "The chance would have been a fine thing! We've walked all the way here from Osmotherley over the hills in rain and mist. All we've seen is each other and he's pointed out some birds!" He ended his delivery with a finger indicating Andrew as the birdwatcher.

Andrew had to reply to counter what seemed like another Martin piss-take.

"Actually, I climbed Roseberry Topping and the view was amazing! This lot were too tired to make it, but I thought I'd go the extra mile, as it were, while they all had a little rest. You know how it is when some members of a team just can't keep up!"

One of the locals decided to enter into a bit of banter. "No, we're not used to seeing teams with members that can't keep up! Round here we've got some real good football clubs you see, so we're used to seeing some good team performances!"

Now Jeremy was in his element. "What do you mean? We've got more teams in the First Division around us than you have! We've got Leicester City, Derby County and Coventry City and all you've got is Newcastle United!"

"But what a team Newcastle is though – they beat Everton 2-1 last Saturday!"

The other local didn't exactly support his colleague by reminding him of Wednesday night's 2-1 defeat of Newcastle by Burnley!

Jeremy, who hadn't been keeping completely up to date with football since the onset of the walk, made the mistake of asking how Derby had gone against Wolverhampton Wanderers on Tuesday night. He looked crestfallen to hear of their 4-0 defeat. Jeremy countered by pondering the district's contribution to Division Two. "In Division Two we've got Nottingham Forest and Notts County only fifteen miles away!"

"We've got Sunderland and Middlesbrough, and Carlisle!"

"If you're going to count Carlisle in your area we're going to claim Hull City, Sheffield Wednesday, Aston Villa and even West Bromwich Albion!" countered Jeremy, thoroughly enjoying himself. It helped that he studied geography at school and knew how ridiculous it was to claim Carlisle as being 'local' to the Teesside district. "Neither of us have much going in the Third, but in the Fourth Division we've got Lincoln City and Mansfield Town. What have you got?"

"We've got Hartlepool and Darlington. But never mind them, we're looking pretty good in the Second Division. I reckon we'll see Middlesbrough go up into the First next season."

Again, Jeremy showed his knowledge of football by giving his opinion as to why Middlesbrough might do so well. "That's because they've got Jack Charlton managing them. I'd say they'd be home and hosed if they had Forest's Duncan McKenzie playing for them as well!"

At this point the two locals played their winning trump card, the elephant in the room as it were: "You've not had much to say about the FA Cup, lads, have you? That was an epic quarter-final encounter against your Nottingham Forest!"

Jeremy had been deliberately avoiding mention of the infamous first quarter-final game held in Newcastle at St James Park on March 9. But now he had no choice.

"Well, we daren't mention it, dare we? I mean, we are scared of retribution aren't we? Let's face it, twenty-three people in hospital, more than a hundred treated at the ground and thirty-nine arrests. More like a war than a football game!"

Chris began to see the danger of pursuing this conversation and added some views of his own, even if those views weren't entirely honest.

"Mind you, I reckon Newcastle should have been given the match without the replay. I mean, both managers agreed to play on and for Newcastle to come back from a two goal and one player deficit to win 4-3 was no mean feat. Now you've beaten Burnley in the semi-final there's nothing stopping you. I reckon Newcastle will beat Liverpool easy in the final!"

The well-known fact that Chris was an avid supporter of Liverpool was kept firmly under the hats of the walkers, who were slowly becoming 'streetwise' enough to recognise potential flashpoints. A completely new sense of respect for Chris was developing.

These remarks seemed to please the two locals. One turned to the other and said: "You seen that bit of graffiti in the men's toilet here in the Holly Bush? The other shook his head in the 'no' direction. "Somebody's scrawled on the wall in big letters 'Jesus Saves' and some wag's written in small letters underneath 'and Keegan knocks in the rebound'! It's funny, but it's a bad omen for us! Anyway, lads, it's been nice talking with you. Hope the weather improves for the rest of your walk and all the best!"

With that the two locals retreated to the bar, leaving the hikers to finish their drinks. Jeremy clapped Chris on the back and congratulated him on his knowledge of 'the game' and for the way he handled the football conversation. Chris in turn quietly admitted he was the one who had added the Kevin Keegan comment to the religious slogan in the toilets, knowing full well it would likely annoy local football supporters! Again, Chris enhanced his position amongst the hikers, who found this revelation very amusing indeed.

Jeremy brought the conversation back to the upcoming walk by sounding a prudent warning about food supplies and Easter.

"Wherever we end up camping, we have to make sure we

have basic food in reserve because most shops will be shut on Easter Sunday. Let's make sandwiches tonight ready for tomorrow's lunch. We may as well be prepared, it's an easy thing to do from the comfort of a hotel room and we have bread to use up."

With that, the hikers returned to their rooms via the fire escape. The first thing they noticed on entering the corridor leading to their rooms was the musty smell of stale clothing trying to dry. On opening the doors to the rooms the walkers were, for the first time, made very aware that a certain aroma accompanied them. This wake-up call dispelled any notion of conquest Robert may have been harbouring for the barmaid, as even he conceded no woman with nostrils that functioned would want to be anywhere near him! The problem was alleviated by opening the windows to refresh the air and by using Jeremy's Brut aerosol deodorant as air freshener.

With some semblance of order re-established, preparations were made for the next day's lunch. Cheese and tomato and strawberry jam sandwiches were made and packed away. Before going to bed, clothes left drying on radiators were readjusted to make sure they were dried evenly by morning. Those with beds retired to the luxury of a soft mattress, sheets and blankets. Those without the comfort of a made-up bed were not long dwelling on it. They were so fatigued that they fell asleep almost immediately. Thank goodness for the Holly Bush Inn!

Chapter 12

Skelton to Staithes

The next morning saw the walkers up and at it by around 7.30am. The first ones to get out of bed began a frantic retrieval of clothes from radiators, both in the rooms and out in the corridor. A glance out of the window proved encouraging, as the sky was clear and just for once wet-weather gear could be packed into rucksacks rather than worn. By about 8.15am, everyone was ready for breakfast and the hikers trouped down into the restaurant area where several hotel guests were finishing eating. The women in charge of breakfast were expecting the seven young men. They must have anticipated their young guests having a healthy appetite because they provided a meal fit for several kings with a choice of cereals, a full English fry-up and toast and marmalade. To say the hikers got their money's worth was an understatement! Not only did they eat all the extra rounds of toast the kind Holly Bush staff put their way, but when the waitresses left the room they even cleared surplus toast from surrounding tables as guests departed the dining room! The hikers were that grateful for the way the women had looked after them, they even left some loose change as a tip!

After breakfast the now ritual preparations for the day's walk began in earnest. Jeremy used money from the kitty to pay for the room and one by one the walkers gathered in the car park. With goodbyes to the women and profound thanks for a superb breakfast the day's walk began.

Finding the official Cleveland Way route was the first priority, which proved very simple. Just a backtrack into Skelton to where the path emerged onto the main street, then a right turn on to Coniston Road.

Now back in Robert's capable hands, the seven were off again heading through Skelton, then across open fields, over a main road and into a wooded valley with Skelton Beck thundering along at the bottom. Recent rains had swollen the stream and the noise of running water accompanied the walkers along this attractive wooded entry to Saltburn. The magnificent railway viaduct crossing this valley made all seven stop in their tracks and ponder the skills of those who had constructed the archways towering high above them.

This wasn't the only bridge in Saltburn to capture the imagination of the hikers. After a pleasant woodland walk, the track emerged on to the street running alongside Skelton Beck. Some distance down this road appeared a derelict iron bridge spanning the valley. Again, the seven gazed in wonder at something that, in contrast, looked unstable and somewhat dangerous. Unbeknown to the group, this bridge, known locally as the Halfpenny Bridge, was indeed due for demolition later in 1974.

Finally, the sea came into view as the road twisted downhill towards Saltburn Sands and the point where Skelton Beck enters the sea. The walk along the seafront in Old Saltburn towards the ancient Ship Inn saw rows of small fishing boats hauled up on the shingle beach. Joe was quick to spot the old Victorian mortuary dated 1881. He pointed out that the seafront location seemed a somewhat strange place to erect a building of this nature. Even at this early time of the morning there were a number of people taking the air along the shingle beach, several fishermen mending nets and quite a few vehicles passing along the coast road.

179

Jeremy was first to comment on what was coming next. "Don't tell me we're going uphill again!"

Robert answered with a smile. "All right, I won't tell you! But you guessed right, Jez, that's where we're going mate, up the path alongside the cliff!"

Today though, the fine weather made such a change that there were no complaints or moans from anyone, except Jeremy, as the walkers began their ascent of the cliff. The path traversed only yards from the edge of the cliff face, beyond which Andrew had already quietly notched up kittiwakes, herring gulls and two 'V' formations of cormorants. Occasionally, stiff-winged seabirds, which were grey and white, circled out from the cliff. Through binoculars the beak looked thicker than usual, with tubular nostrils. A quick skim through the pages of the bird book devoted to seabirds soon revealed these to be fulmar petrels, which were another new bird for Andrew's ever growing list.

At one point, the walkers stopped and looked back towards Saltburn and beyond. Now for the first time the skies were clear enough to see Teesside in all its industrial glory. Jeremy was quite perturbed and somewhat depressed by the smoke and fumes emanating from the numerous chimneys. Everyone agreed, though, that it was an impressive display of Britain's industrial might, despite the obvious air pollution.

"Don't you think we live in a fantastic country? On the one hand, we've got industry giving us material things and jobs and all that, but on the other there's open spaces like this where you can still see wildlife in all its glory. I reckon we're very lucky and I hope we can have both industry and wild places forever!" said an obviously moved Andrew.

Andreas spotted something unusual in the foreground. "What's that little box thing moving down the hill in front of the hotels in Saltburn? Can I borrow your binoculars, Andrew?"

Andreas took the binoculars and studied the peculiar moving object before letting everyone else have a look. The general opinion was that it was some sort of tramcar designed to get people from the hotel area on flat ground high above the sea at Saltburn, down to the beach or on to the pier. Andrew found no reference to it in the guidebook, so the people transport explanation seemed most logical, although everyone agreed the device must be fairly old.

The track continued up Hunt Cliff and around the side of Warsett Hill, running for a while alongside a railway line. At this point, Joseph called for a toilet break and disappeared behind some hawthorn bushes. Andreas followed, calling out that, like Joe, he too needed to 'point Percy at the porcelain'.

"What you on about, 'Dreas? You're not going to find any porcelain to aim at round here!" chided Robert.

"Where did he get that from?" asked Andrew, who didn't have the unrestricted access to television available to the other hikers.

"It's from *Steptoe and Son*. Percy's the name some supposed Australian relative of theirs gave to his whatsit!" explained Robert. He continued. "You know what, I'm going to give mine a name that will forever remind me of the Cleveland Way! Thanks to the number of times Joseph drags his out to have a pee, from now on it's called Joseph, or Joe for short!"

Martin was quick to respond. "Well we know all your girlfriends will get to know Joe, but I bet they'll never think to call it Joseph!"

Fortunately, there were enough people separating the twins to prevent a full-blown conflict, but it was a close call.

Robert raised some chuckles by announcing – just loud enough for Joseph to hear – that he was just going to point Joseph at the John, before he too disappeared behind the bushes.

The real Joseph emerged grumbling about being taken advantage of and how it wasn't appropriate for Robert to be taking the piss out of his name.

"I'm not taking the piss out of your name, Joe, in fact Joseph is doing an excellent job taking the piss out of me!" came Robert's retort from behind the bushes, which seemed to generate some amusement from everyone present.

The walkers continued onward and found themselves descending towards the village of Skinningrove. On the hill above the town was an enormous rusty looking building. Andrew was able to inform the group, thanks to Bill Cowley's guidebook, that what they were looking at was an iron and steelworks, although it appeared strangely still and silent.

"Maybe it's all closed up for Easter," commented Robert.

"Well, if that's the case, why is there still smoke pouring out of Teesside? Maybe this place has closed down permanently?" asked Martin, but nobody could provide any answers.

The walking track then descended to Cattersty Sands, passing in front of what was obviously a mountain of slag. The material looked as if it had been poured directly from the mouth of a volcano and had formed unusual patterns on the cliff face. Surprisingly, among vegetation sprouting from the base of this man-made mountain was a pair of stonechats. The male was splendidly red and stood out in stark contrast to the grey rock behind. This was yet another new bird for Andrew, who did his best to inspire interest from everyone else, but it wasn't forthcoming!

The walkers then passed through a concrete jetty and continued on towards the surprising rows of houses that make up Skinningrove. Surprising, because it seemed a strange place to build industrial style, terraced housing, so close to what must once have been a beautiful secluded bay. Alongside the houses were allotments balanced precariously on the hillside. These allotments included wooden pigeon lofts, home to the tightly grouped flocks of racing pigeons wheeling above the town.

"Are we going to eat here?" asked Joseph, aware that it was perhaps a bit early for lunch, but he was hungry yet again.

After general discussion it was agreed lunch would be served at the top of the highest cliff in England, Boulby Cliff, which was going to be the next major challenge faced by the hikers on today's walk.

Once again, the intrepid walkers found themselves climbing from sea level to lofty heights. In this instance, lofty heights just behind the town of Loftus! The twisting and undulating track took the group past ancient alum workings on the edge of the cliffs – quarries that formed the basis of some of England's earliest, truly industrial, activity. While the hikers could plainly tell the site was adulterated by mankind, they would have been genuinely amazed to hear the full story of alum manufacture and its use as a fixative in clothing dyes. Had they known that copious quantities of human urine were involved in the chemistry of alum manufacture and that all this urine was brought here from the cramped towns of the North-East, they would have had renewed respect for something the seven walkers were famous for, namely 'taking the piss'. This simple phrase, which perfectly summed up fifty per cent of the conversation between the seven, was indeed coined by the people responsible for providing urine to the alum dye industry.

At one point on the way up Boulby Cliff, Jeremy found the prospect of another descent into a gully, followed by an obvious ascent up the other side, too much to bear.

"Not down again, please! You know what that means don't you?"

The remark was addressed to everyone, but Andreas was

the one who replied.

"Well go on then, Jez! What does it mean?" he enquired.

Between gasps for breath, Jeremy replied. "It means we've got to go up again, like the old saying says!"

A bemused Andreas, after some consideration of the statement answered. "No, Jez, the old saying is 'what goes up must come down', not the other way round!"

After a couple of minutes of hard walking both down, then severely up again, Andreas was heard bitterly remarking. "You know what, Jeremy might be right 'cos on this walk it does seem to be what goes down must go up and vice-versa, with rapid monotony and regularity!"

Lunch was held in grand style on the top of Boulby Cliff, with a fine view into the valley beyond, leading to the quaint village of Staithes. Unfortunately, it was not without incident, despite the fact it was one of the better prepared feasts on the walk. The problem was that Joseph missed out on a strawberry jam sandwich! Hardly an earth-shattering event to be fair, but with everyone getting tired and perhaps a little irritated by each other's company, it escalated into full-blown conflict. Robert decided to rub it in that he had enjoyed two strawberry jam sandwiches – in fact, he was eating one as he made this bold statement! Normally, Joseph, the Christian, the man of peace and the one most likely to travel on a 'peace train', would have failed to react – but not this time. To say the attack took Robert by surprise was very much an understatement. One minute Robert was cramming the last jam sandwich into his mouth, smiling and saying something like: "Guess what, Joe, I've had two and this is one of them!" The next, he was spinning across the ridge with an enraged Christian thumping the crap out of him. The remainder of the jam sandwich was sent spinning off into a blackberry bush, no doubt providing succour for the local wildlife when some furry or feathered being eventually found it.

"Drag him off me! Drag him off me, for Christ's sake, drag him off me!" an enraged and defensive Robert could be heard screaming beneath the parka-clad demon sitting on top of him and trying hard to land a punch.

"You bastard, Robert. You rotten bastard. I've been looking forward to one of them sandwiches all morning. It's bad enough you pinching other people's women, but taking my jam sandwich is the limit!"

At this point, the other walkers managed to drag Joseph away and restore order. He was immediately apologetic and a surprised Robert, in uncharacteristically diplomatic form, let the incident pass. Chris, after a period of laughter, recognised the signs of imminent group collapse and made a firm announcement.

"Well, this proves we're getting tired. Tomorrow is Easter Sunday and I reckon we should ease up a bit. We're treating this walk like a race, which isn't what it's supposed to be! I say we get to Staithes, find a campsite and in the morning we don't rush to get off to the next place."

Andrew, on the other hand, wanted to keep the pressure on and maintain the pace. But this time he was outnumbered and the decision was made to sleep in on Sunday morning before continuing to Whitby.

After the eventful lunch, the hikers continued past the small settlement of Boulby, along tiny roads and across fields towards the edge of Staithes Beck. The track then descended into the quaintly beautiful harbour town of Staithes. This ancient little town with its historic links to Captain Cook left the seven walkers spellbound. The place was so unlike the villages and towns of Leicestershire and so tightly packed into the natural confines of the Staithes Beck valley that it seemed to transport the hikers back in time. The presence of small fishing craft with old sea hands doing maintenance work, the smell of the sea and the call of herring gulls as the group crossed the bridge into the first part of the town suggested a different era. It was as if time had stood still. If a colourful character with one leg, smoking a clay pipe with a parrot on his shoulder had hobbled past, it would have seemed normal and in keeping with the scene!

Upon entering the main street, the hikers were confronted with the modern world again. There, immediately alongside them, was a coffee bar called the Singing Kettle – a coffee bar with about a dozen flash motorbikes parked outside and the Slade track 'Cum on feel the Noize' playing loudly on the jukebox inside.

There was no argument or discussion. The group went straight in and, despite sour glances from a large gathering of leather-clad bikers, commandeered a table in the window for themselves. After an anguished unburdening of rucksacks, the hikers ordered food and drink. Maybe not enough to stop eating again later on, but at least enough for Joseph to stop thinking about the jam sandwiches he had missed out on earlier! Enquiries at the counter revealed the position of a campsite at the top edge of Staithes, so this was to be their next port of call. Jeremy was quick to point out that they would have to go uphill again, confirming his rewriting of the old maxim of 'what goes up must come down' as, yet again, they were doing the opposite!

While waiting for the food and drinks to arrive at the table, Andrew and Andreas approached the jukebox, which was obviously the 'domain' of the leather-clad bikies. Andreas decided to put coins in and select some music. Until this point, Andrew had always had faith in Andreas. After all, Andreas watched all the latest TV programmes, most of which Andrew was banned from in case he was perverted from a steadfast journey towards hard work in the poultry industry! Andrew watched Andreas put the coins in, watched him press D4 on the jukebox and then cast his eye to the playlist to see what Andreas had selected. A feeling of horror shook Andrew's very soul. Admittedly, Andrew was not that streetwise with regard to music, but even he knew that any song by Little Jimmy Osmond was not the correct selection for an upbeat coffee bar frequented by some of the toughest looking motorbike riding individuals Andrew had ever seen!

"Andreas, do you know what you've just put on! Do you really know?" a panic-stricken Andrew urgently whispered in the spotty ear of his Greek mate.

"Yeah, course I do! The Rolling Stones and 'It's All Over Now'. That should go down well – you know, make us look hard!"

An increasingly stressed Andrew pointed at the buttons Andreas had just pressed. Andreas looked at the numbers and then disbelievingly at the playlist. Both then watched the jukebox as his record began to be selected by the visible mechanism.

"Oh, my God! What have I done?" exclaimed a mortified Andreas.

Their eyes met in mutual horror as both began to remember the tune and words of what they were about to hear. The record had only recently been released. To be frank, it was a catchy little tune and easy to sing along to, but it certainly was the very last bit of music leather-clad bikers would have chosen, even on a bad day! Almost instantly, together, and without rehearsal or hesitation, Andrew and Andreas returned rapidly to the table and tried to hide themselves among the group. The workings of the jukebox continued inexorably onward until the distinctive sound of Jimmy Osmond could be heard:

'I'm gonna knock on your door, ring on yer bell,
Tap on yer window too.
If you don't come out tonight when the moon is bright,
I'm gonna knock and ring and tap until you do.'

Conversation amongst the hikers stopped and faces turned towards Andrew and Andreas, who by now were looking at the floor for any cracks large enough to hide in. From the coffee bar came that creaking sound made only by twisting leather, as twelve motorbike riders turned, *en masse*, to examine the newcomers in the Singing Kettle. Apart from Little Jimmy belting out his catchy tune there was an omnipresent silence and a stillness in the café. When the song finally came to a halt, three of the bikers went to the machine and piled in coins, ensuring that a steady flow of heavy rock music followed. Slowly 'normality' began to creep back into the café.

Andreas leaned forward. "I knew if I did that they would go and stick loads of money in and we would get some decent music for free. See, I knew what I was doing all along!"

Nobody believed him.

Naturally the remaining time spent in the café was some-what uncomfortable for the hikers. A feeling of relief swept over the seven as they emerged into the late afternoon light.

"Right, let's get tonight's campsite sorted," suggested Robert, already leading the way up the narrow street heading inland.

Towards the top of the hill was the sign they had been told to watch out for: Holiday Fellowship Centre Campsite, with an arrow pointing up a narrow lane. Alongside the lane was a serried row of World War One army barracks, now turned into holiday bunkhouses. Andreas stepped forward to knock on the door of the reception building, which was now closed. Inside was obviously the home of the manager, as lights were on and voices could be heard. As he stepped forward the band members began singing Little Jimmy Osmond's 'I'm Gonna Knock on Your Door', which caused some amusement to everyone, bar Andreas.

After some time, a friendly gentleman emerged from the reception building and gladly relieved the hikers of a few pounds for the privilege of pitching their tents in the paddock beyond the huts. A short walk away from their camping ground, next to the buildings, was a somewhat bleak, but functional, concrete toilet and shower block.

With tents pitched and ablutions well utilised, the seven felt part of the human race again, although in all honesty their clothing was stained and in need of a wash. Nobody could face walking down into Staithes as obviously it would ultimately mean walking back up again. As darkness fell, the stoves were lit and a simple home-cooked meal produced. Another early night followed, with the prospect of a lie-in on Sunday morning. Just what the doctor ordered!

Chapter 13

Staithes to Whitby

Andreas was first to stir on Easter Sunday morning. Andreas was first to stir most mornings but, as if in testimony to how tired the hikers had become, even he was amazed to see what time it was.

"Hey, fellas!"

No response from either Andrew or Chris.

"Hey, fellas! Fellas! It's sodding ten o'clock!!"

From the next tent came the voice of Martin.

"Shut up, 'Dreas, go back to sleep".

But it was too late. Andrew awoke and was horrified.

"Bloody hell, it's ten o'clock! Ten o'bloody clock! We've got to get to Whitby today!"

Andrew started to get organised, as did Andreas and Chris. Slowly but surely, the sense of urgency pervaded the rest of the hikers and gradually everyone slipped into the well-rehearsed routine of ablutions, breakfast and dismantling the camp. The day was cool, fine and breezy – another ideal walking day presented itself.

Examining the map revealed a fairly ambitious day's hike, especially after such a late start. By the time the entire group were fully ready to march it was 11am. Andrew was determined to see the harbour at Staithes before walking off towards Whitby. The previous night they had only seen the edge of Staithes seafront, so Andrew convinced Robert that they needed to go down to the sea before beginning the Cleveland Walk proper. This bit of down before up could have been avoided, and probably would have been if Jeremy had examined the map, but it was well worth the effort. The walk along the harbourside, passing fishing nets and quaint tiny cottages, was delightful and left a great impression on all the walkers. The sign for the Cleveland Way walk, at the south-eastern edge of Staithes seafront, pointed ominously back uphill, bringing groans from everyone as stiff muscles were only just limbering up.

All too soon though, the track left the built-up edge of Staithes and crossed over open fields, heading towards the steep sides of Blackberry Wyke, where a kestrel was hovering, 'standing on air' looking for some earthbound furry mite.

Joseph was preoccupied. He had started thinking of Yvonne again and desperately wanted to find a phone box. Agreement was reached that tonight in Whitby would be phone home night – it was Easter after all. Joseph was hoping to resurrect his failing relationship with Yvonne and tonight was going to be the night.

The small settlement of Port Mulgrave stimulated some interest, especially after they met a local fisherman about to descend Rosedale Cliffs. The thick-set Yorkshireman was carrying a long fishing rod and a hamper, presumably containing fishing gear and lunch.

"What you hoping to catch?" asked Martin as the man crossed in front of them.

"Well, lads, thee never knows thee luck! I allus tries fer cod, like, but if t'conditions are reet I'll go fer bass or pollock. Depends on t'tide an' t'weather. Wot you lads up to then? Looks like yous bin wanderin' fer a while!"

Martin replied: "We're walking the Cleveland Way. We started in Helmsley last Monday. We're carrying all our camping gear and tonight we're stopping in Whitby. Anything you reckon we should see in Whitby?"

"Whitby? Aye, it's grand. As ye walks in ye'll see t'Captain Cook statue; the harbour's worth a look, so is the old swing bridge in't middle o' town. Whatever ye does, though, don't miss out on't famous local food – cod an' chips wi' mushy peas, along wi' a slice of bread and butter an' a cuppa tea. Ye can't beat it! Good luck, lads."

With that he was off through a gate and down an obscure track towards the sea and the old pier and jetty at Port Mulgrave, where ironstone from the Grinkle mine was once loaded. The walking track took the seven along Lingrow Cliffs and into the village of Runswick where, in the late 1600s, the entire village bar one house slipped into the sea, fortunately, without loss of life. Time was marching on and so, too, were the walkers, who were becoming increasingly aware of just how much they had taken on that day.

"We're pushing it today, aren't we?" commented a tired and anxious Joseph. In fairness, all seven hikers were hurting and, despite fantastic views across Runswick Bay, were more concerned with progress than the aesthetic qualities of the district. Even conversation was stymied in an attempt to save energy for the next step and the next breath. The walk sank down to Runswick Sands. Walking along the beach was delightful, but provided a few anxious moments for Andrew and Robert as they struggled to locate the path up Hob Holes. Once found, it took them along the cliff edge to Kettleness, again alongside evidence of old human activity in the form of alum and ironstone mines and a disused railway line. At Kettleness, the track skirted Kettleness farmyard before winding around the cliffs again. It was here that Andrew spotted one of the more exciting birds on the trip. Soaring parallel to them was a peregrine falcon. Flying with powerful purpose, it struck fear into seagulls, pigeons and jackdaws that could be seen flying away as fast as they could. Just for once the entire group stopped and showed interest in this beautiful and exciting bird.

Further on from the small settlement of Kettleness, the old railway disappeared into a tunnel. Robert pointed out that it should re-appear as the walkers got closer to Sandsend. On the map the route of the old track was shown emerging from the hillside just before more old quarries to the north of Sandsend. Heads down and onward again, along cliffs, down small valleys and up small hills, the seven marched on. The track then caught up with the railway again, just as Robert had predicted, as it reappeared from the surprisingly long tunnel.

"It's amazing to think that tunnel would have been dug by hand. All that work and now it just sits here doing nothing! It would be a fantastic train ride if it was still open, don't you reckon?" commented Chris, who had obviously inherited some of his history teacher father's fascination with antiquity.

Just as interesting were the old alum workings, some dating to before the seventeenth century, found around Sandsend Ness. The almost alien landscape created by quarrying proved fascinating and more precious time was taken examining the hills and hollows made by our industrious ancestors.

In the distance, past Sandsend, could be seen Whitby and high on the hill the ruins of Whitby Abbey.

"Come on, we've got to get to Whitby tonight and we've got to find somewhere to camp," urged an anxious Andrew, who really liked to be settled into a campsite before the daylight disappeared.

Onward again they went, with heads bowed and legs in automatic mode. The walk into Sandsend was made easier by being on the bed of the old railway. Past Sandsend, in fading light, the decision was made to walk along the beach, at least as far as the outskirts of Whitby. Through sheer exhaustion, the seven walkers strung out in a long line pacing ever onward without conversation or comment. Each walker was lost in his own thoughts of the walk so far and of their own uncertain futures.

Just before the northern-most outskirts of Whitby, where a small stream leaves the golf course and enters the sea, the walkers gathered again.

"This is where we are," said Robert, indicating their location on the map.

"Perhaps we had better head up the hill and enter the town on the edge at the top? I mean, what we need is a campsite and we won't find one here on the beach. Keep your eyes open as we head into town," Robert continued.

Jeremy wondered if the map gave any clues as to the whereabouts of camping facilities. A quick look did show a caravan/campsite out past the abbey on the other side of town.

So it was decided to continue on into Whitby and if no campsite showed itself then they would have no choice, but to go beyond the abbey to the Saltwick Bay camping ground.

Walking through a large town was a different experience. The streets were fairly busy despite it being Easter Sunday. In the failing light there looked to be the prospect of a night out, once their tents had been erected and once they had managed to clean themselves up a bit. The statue in honour of Captain Cook was duly noted. The whalebone archway ceremoniously passed through, as if this ritual was part and parcel of the Cleveland Way. The hikers then tramped into the middle of Whitby and over the famous old swing bridge next to the Dolphin Hotel. The narrow streets with shop windows displaying Whitby jet and seaside postcards were noticed but, again, all that could be considered at this stage was finding a campsite.

At the end of Church Street, at the very start of Henrietta Street, emerged the 199 steps that famously climb up to the abbey and St Mary's church. With darkness now descending, all seven climbed up the steps without complaint. Once at the top, the map was consulted under a streetlight and the decision was taken to leave the Cleveland Way proper, in favour of the safety of Abbey Lane and Hawsker Lane. The walkers could have followed the Cleveland Way along the top of the cliffs to the Saltwick campsite, but by now it was dark enough for this clifftop path to be dangerous.

Andreas took out his torch and a somewhat excited group trudged on to find the camp – excited by the prospect of returning later to the bright lights of Whitby and the cod and chip supper mentioned by the fisherman at Port Mulgrave (with mushy peas, a slice of bread and a pot of tea, naturally).

Yet again, Andreas was the member of the group who reached forward to knock on the reception door at Saltwick Bay campsite. Yet again, he endured a chorus of 'I'm Going to Knock on Your Door' for his trouble.

Despite the scruffy appearance of the seven walkers, they were made very welcome by the middle-aged couple running the campsite. They were shown to a quiet section of a field set aside for campers and allowed to pitch their tents. This time great effort was made, in the fairly new shower block, to really get sparkly clean. Only the cleanest clothes were put on as that night was set to be an historic one, where the men of Leicestershire meet the women of Yorkshire. Unfortunately, at this stage the cleanest clothes weren't very clean and, despite intense optimism, their chances of success with any members of the opposite sex were severely compromised. Not that any of the seven were aware of this fact! Within an hour of arriving at the campsite, tents pitched and divested of their rucksacks, the seven hungry young men began their grand return to the bustling harbour town of Whitby.

"I really don't know how you two do it," Jeremy remarked, looking at the Jenkins twins.

"You've both been getting ready for town, making yourselves look like chick magnets, and in the end you look identical. Do you follow a manual or something?"

Remarkably enough, Jeremy was right. After an hour's fumbling in the dark for clothes, hurried washing in the toilet block and frantic brushing of reluctant tousled hair, the twins had emerged dressed identically. Only those who really knew them would have been able to tell them apart.

"The ladies will soon realise the difference between us when we take our clothes off, Jez!" added Robert with a cheeky twinkle in his eye.

"Yes, they'll get quite a shock when they see little Joe!" added Martin, much to everyone's amusement, apart from the real Joseph of course.

"You mean you've got clean enough underwear to risk taking your pants off in anybody's company other than ours, Rob?" asked an incredulous Joseph. "If your undies are anything like mine, you've really got to hope any females you pick up tonight have lost their sense of smell."

"It's worse than that for me," complained Andrew. "If I get lucky she needs to have no sense of smell and no eyesight either. After what happened in Great Ayton, the visual appearance of my underwear hasn't exactly improved!"

Robert continued in fine sarcastic form. "Well, we needn't worry about that Andy need we? You've as much chance of succeeding with some young female tonight as a one-legged man trying to win an arse kicking competition! I mean, you haven't found a girl yet who's let you anywhere near her, so what makes you think tonight's the night?"

Martin rallied to Andrew's defence – well, sort of. "Leave him alone, Rob. There's bound to be some ugly woman out there who'll let him get close to her one of these days! You know, some old dear with a screwed up face like a bulldog chewing on a wasp!"

"Thanks a million, fellas. With friends like you lot who needs enemies?" Andrew muttered.

Andreas was getting impatient and, as he held the torch, it was prudent to follow him closely.

"Hang on, 'Dreas, we are coming too!" announced Chris as he finished zipping up the tent and splashing some of Jeremy's Brut aftershave on his whiskerless face. Despite miles of hiking, dirty clothes and a scruffy appearance, even Chris was experiencing a flush of testosterone as Whitby beckoned. The imagined charms of hundreds of waiting Yorkshire maidens, offering plates of cod, chips and mushy peas and clutching cricket bats signed by Geoff Boycott fired his imagination.

"Hey, Chris! It's all very well splashing Jeremy's Brut 'all over', but you're supposed to shave first!" Robert was in fine piss-take form and it seemed no one was immune. "I bet you're not bothered about the state of your pants if you get to remove them in female company are you, Chris? You just don't want her to notice you haven't reached puberty yet!"

Chris found a way of shutting him up though. With a deft shake of his wrist, Robert received an overdose of Brut that would have embarrassed even Henry Cooper, who famously 'splashed it all over' in the TV adverts. "There you go, Rob, see how you do tonight. I mean 'nothing beats the great smell of Brut!' Now we'll be able to find out if the stuff really works, won't we!"

Andreas found the situation highly amusing. "Well done, Chris. You've gotta fight fire with fire!"

"Unless you're a fireman!" Joseph added as a punchline.

In high spirits, and sharing some witty banter and repartee, the walkers began the return journey to Whitby. Relieved of rucksacks, the walk back to town seemed remarkably easy, even joyful. It was testimony to their youth and their fitness that contemplating heading back into Whitby – only to be followed by the inevitable walk back to the campsite – wasn't at all daunting to the seven explorers.

"We need a phone box!" announced Joseph, who seemed supremely confident that things would go well as Yvonne was bound to be home with her mum on the evening of Easter Sunday, guaranteeing a lengthy conversation with her.

The descent down the 199 steps was enlivened by checking on the accuracy of the claim that there were actually 199 steps. The view over the harbour was superbly lit by street lights and the lights emanating from whatever shops were still trading. On to Henrietta Street and then Church street, where Joseph spotted a 1901 Wesleyan Hall.

"Maybe we should go to a service, I mean it's a religious night after all?" Joseph enquired of the group.

The statement failed to get a meaningful reply, especially after Robert noticed one of the engravings in the bricks of the old chapel.

"No Joseph, we are looking for greater things tonight, just like this gentleman did, and indeed, found!"

Joseph didn't fully understand. "What are you on about, Robert?"

"Well, look on this brick, it says 'Laid. Mr. E Hemingway'. He obviously got lucky and so will I. Come on, onward to fish and chips!" Robert exclaimed expansively.

Joseph examined the plaque, one of many on the chapel wall. "It means he's buried here somewhere and you know it, and are we really having fish and chips again? We've lived on the bloomin' stuff!"

"But these are Whitby fish and chips!" Jeremy reminded the group of the distinct pedigree given to the town's speciality dish.

"Don't forget thee slices of bread and butter and cuppa tea, like, and afterwards a walk in t'woods, like, along t'track wi' yer friends, like!" said Andreas in a very reasonable imitation of the Yorkshire accent they were growing rather fond of hearing.

By now, the seven had crossed the swing bridge and were heading along Pier Road. A restaurant was selected and seven servings of all things deemed a delicacy in Whitby were placed before them.

Martin decided to attempt to chat up the young waitress who delivered their cod and chips.

"We're walking the Cleveland Way!" he began in fine confident form, but wrecked it by adding: "Do you come here often?"

A cheery female voice responded. "Of course I come 'ere of'en! I bleedin' work 'ere, don't I? Do you want any sauce?"

Robert muscled into the conversation. "You've just given him some sauce, sweetheart! What are you doing after work? Would you like to show us the sights of Whitby?"

"After work I'm goin' to bed! I haven't time fer sightseeing! What sauce can I get you?"

Robert persisted. "Bed works for me! Your place or mine?"

"Oh, Gordon Bennett, here we go!" Joseph put his head in his hands then looked up at the young waitress. "We're not all like him, some of us would treat you with respect and not insult you with such pathetic chat-up lines."

Andreas decided his time had come and used one of the lines he had recently seen on television. With exaggerated movement he licked the end of his finger, and then lightly brushed the tight skirt of the waitress. Looking into her eyes he said: "Forget this lot, come back to my tent and we'll get you out of those wet clothes!"

Luckily the young lady was well versed in dealing with frisky groups of young men. She quickly tried to steer the conversation into safer territory.

"Look 'ere, I'm the one supposed to be givin' you sauce, not t'other way round! Anyway, why are you walkin' the Cleveland Way? What you doin' that for?"

A momentary silence followed. It was a good question. All the lofty ideals brought up at planning meetings about this being the last time the group would ever be together, seemed to have been forgotten in the constant struggle to cover miles and keep fed and comfortable. In a way, they were living day-to-day with only the finish line at Filey uppermost in their minds.

Robert, still clinging to the dream of some sort of bond with the waitress, provided something of an answer: "Just for a laugh, we just thought we'll have a laugh!"

Martin grabbed another chance at gaining the humour high ground.

"For the halibut! Trouble is, we've ended up with cod!"

"Are you two twins?" the waitress asked, finally realising the similarities between Martin and Robert.

"You've got to admit, they breed 'em observant up north don't they?" remarked Jeremy, who went on to add, "Can we please have some tomato sauce and some vinegar?"

With that, the waitress saw her means of escape and located some sauces before getting back to her work.

On cue, the seven dived into their meals, which were indeed a considerable cut above your average and confirmed Whitby's standing as the fish and chip capital of the UK. Combined with the slices of buttered white bread, the pale green splodge of mushy peas and the piping hot cup of tea, the meal was indeed a fine one.

"There's something I've noticed about the way they serve tea in Yorkshire!" announced Jeremy, as if he had found some important culinary secret. "They always give you a pot of tea and a separate one of boiled water to top up your pot when you've had your first cup! Its brilliant and it makes the rest of your tea drinking more consistent and pleasurable!"

For his trouble, Jeremy received a long quiet stare from the rest of the group. The silence was broken by Joseph in unusually ironic tones: "I didn't realise you could be so profound, Jez! No really, there's a side to you that very few ever get to see and, you know what, we are all feeling privileged to hear such words of wisdom. Do you have any more statements like that, oh great one? Pray share them with us!"

Jeremy rose to the occasion. "Yeah, there is another. Sod off, Joseph! Go jump in a lake!"

Realising the futility of chasing after the waitress, and feeling replete after their meal, the seven wandered out into the night and continued down towards the sea. Walking to the end of the harbour wall on West Pier found the group staring down at the cold dark waters of the North Sea.

"I wonder if Captain Cook ever came down here and stared back at Whitby when he lived here?" asked Chris. "You know, we're probably standing in the same spot he did hundreds of years ago."

Andrew wasn't so sure. "I doubt he was in this exact spot, because the concrete looks pretty new to me! If Captain Cook ever stood here, I reckon he would have got wet feet. Actually, he would have been swimming!"

Chris continued in historical theme. "Nevertheless, he was a remarkable man wasn't he? Three trips he made to the South Pacific before he finally got killed."

Joseph could see some humorous potential and asked, "Yes, Chris, and on which one of the three trips did he die?"

Chris snapped back: "His last one, you prat! His last one!"

"Just testing, just testing!" Joe replied sarcastically.

Andreas, who was used to seeing warm, clear waters on his trips back to Greece with his parents, was studying the sea rising and falling outside the harbour walls.

"The water doesn't look very appealing does it? You wouldn't get me eating anything that's come out of there!"

Andrew was quick to shatter his illusions. "You just have mate! You had cod and chips and that's where the cod came from!"

Joseph was getting impatient. "Come on, fellas, let's find a phone. I want to ring Yvonne."

"Yeah, let's find a phone, I need to call home and let Dad know where we are so he can pick us up in Filey on time. When do you reckon we'll get there?" Andrew asked.

Robert pointed out they still had to reach Robin Hood's Bay, then Scarborough and then Filey. After some discussion, it was decided to have an easy day on Easter Monday —mainly because Robert was convinced he would be lying in bed with some beautiful Whitby girl and didn't want to be rushed in the morning.

"So, we're going to be walking to Robin Hood's Bay tomorrow, Scarborough on Tuesday, which means we get to Filey on Wednesday. We can book my dad to pick us up mid to late afternoon on Wednesday at Filey Brigg. Does that sound

OK to everyone?" Andrew asked, wanting to be quite sure everyone realised what needed to be done, even if Robert did find some dusky maiden in Whitby!

Agreement was reached and the seven trouped back into town. A phone box was located and Andrew went in first. A quick call ensued, during which the pick-up day and time was confirmed. He reassured his family he was eating well and staying out of trouble and confirmed that the walk was fantastic, even though it was harder than any of them had imagined!

As Andrew emerged, only Joseph and Martin were waiting.

"Where are they all?" Andrew asked.

"In the pub next to the swing bridge. You can't miss it – just follow the smell of Brut!" suggested Martin, who had agreed to wait whilst Joseph made his phone call. This was just as well, because Joseph was about to get some heartbreaking news.

Andrew wandered off and joined the others, who had found a warm cosy bar with a landlord who didn't ask how old they were. Not only that, but on the next table were three pretty girls, about their age, with an older woman sharing some sort of celebration. Robert and Jeremy were already in conversation with two of the girls.

"So, which one of you has a birthday then?" Robert asked.

"It's me! I'm eighteen today. My mum is here, that's her look!" With that she waved at the older woman who, on closer inspection, looked much older. Much, much, older. Maybe it was the untidy hair or the wrinkled face, or maybe it was the way she held her cigarette as she waved back – hanging from her mouth with a saggy droop. Frankly, it was hard to believe the eighteen-year-old was any relation. Maybe the women of Whitby have such a hard life they age prematurely, thought Robert as he politely waved back.

"That's me baby sister, Caroline!" Another wave to a girl a

couple of years younger, but who was, nevertheless, drinking rum and coke. "And that's me best friend Jackie, come to make sure I get home safe and don't get dragged into the bushes by strangers from the south!"

"Don't worry, the night is young and by the time I drag you off I won't be a stranger anymore, will I?" said Robert, optimistically. "What's your name, anyway? Mine's Robert and this is my friend Jeremy!" As he said 'I'm Robert' he held his hands about twelve inches apart, but he reduced this 'size' to about four inches as he introduced his 'friend Jeremy'. Robert's eyes were sparkling with suggestive intent!

"You're a bit of a beggar aren't you, Robert?" she said with a giggle. "I'm Melanie."

At this point, her friend Jackie came over and straightaway confronted Robert, as if to scare him off and stop Melanie's birthday party being taken over by some stranger.

"Can I ask you a question?" she didn't wait for Robert to answer. "Are you homosexual?"

Robert was somewhat taken aback and gave a quick honest answer.

"No. Why do you ask?"

"Well, in my experience of men, only my homosexual friends go out at night with that much aftershave on! I can smell you from over there. Do you sell it or something?"

Jeremy decided to step into the fray.

"Hello, ladies, I'm Jeremy…"

But that's as far as he got because his interjection was seen as an opportunity for everyone else to present their credentials.

"Hi, I'm Andrew."

"Hello, I'm Chris."

"Ignore all these, my name's Andreas and I've got a Greek penis!"

What possessed Andreas to say that was never fully explained, but it caused the longest, most awkward silence known to have ever occurred in a Whitby pub. Robert could see no hope of recovery and decided it was time for a toilet break.

"OK, well sorry ladies, but I've got to point Joseph at the John! I'll leave you two with these smooth-talking fellas, who incidentally I've never seen before!"

With that he was gone.

Andrew broke the silence in an effort to stop Jackie from staring open-mouthed at Andreas. Clearly she was having difficulty recovering from his comment.

"Don't mind, Andreas, he can't help saying things like that. In his spare time he's a master baker of some repute!"

Melanie, meanwhile, was pondering Robert's departing words.

"What did he mean 'point Joseph at the John?'" she innocently enquired.

"He means his thingy-ma-jig! He's given it a name. He's gone for a pee so he's aiming it at the toilet. You know, the John! Don't you watch American TV shows, Mel?"

In a subdued tone and addressed to Melanie alone, Jackie continued: "Tell you what, though, this lot are seriously weird, Melanie. They've got a fixation on their naughty bits! There's something deeply wrong with the lot of 'em!"

As if to confirm just how weird this group of young men were, Robert came straight back into the bar, except it wasn't Robert! Oh sure, Andrew, Jeremy, Chris and Andreas knew it wasn't Robert and that instead it was Martin, but none of the ladies knew that. At this point, they didn't know Martin existed and just assumed that Robert had returned from a lavatory visit somewhat prematurely.

Martin was visibly stressed. "Fellas, quick, come with me, I can't get Joseph out! He's just shrivelled up in there and won't budge! I need at least one of you to help me drag him out!"

Andrew and Andreas immediately looked concerned and flustered. On the way out of the bar they gleaned from Martin that poor old Joseph had phoned Yvonne, only to be ditched. No amount of pleading from Joe would persuade Yvonne to allow him to come and see her when he got home. No way was he to telephone ever again. Their relationship was over forthwith and right now. Do not pass go and do not collect £200. Bye, bye and good riddance!

Joseph was indeed in a mess. He was slumped on the floor of the phone box with tears streaming down his face.

"Hey, Joe, come on mate, come on. You can't stay there all night!" Martin said encouragingly.

"Yeah, come on, Joseph, it's better to have loved and lost than never to have loved at all." added Andrew, who quite frankly was way out of his depth.

Joseph looked up at that comment.

"Wouldn't I just love to meet the dickhead who first said that. He obviously didn't know true love, he didn't know pure love and he definitely didn't know Yvonne." Head down sobbing into a dirty hanky, Joseph remained slumped in the phone box.

"Well go on, 'Dreas, this is one of those moments when some appropriate quote from the TV might just help. I mean, we've got to get him outta there haven't we?" Martin said to Andreas.

Andreas pushed his face to the glass next to Joseph. Joe looked up and made eye contact with Andreas, who simply said: "In the words of Telly Savalas's *Kojak*: 'Who loves ya baby'. Bear that in mind, Joseph."

Joseph's eyes turned downward again, only this time his head was shaking in disbelief.

"Brilliant, Andreas, just brilliant! I mean what the hell was that supposed to signify?" Martin asked incredulously.

"I dunno, it just seemed appropriate and you've got to admit, it is a quote from the telly and it does sort of fit, doesn't it?" Andreas answered, not quite grasping the problem.

"Andreas, you are unbelievable!" Martin replied.

"Thanks, mate," said Andreas, completely misjudging the emphasis of Martin's reply.

"Meanwhile, back at the bar, Chris had realised what was going on in the minds of the young ladies. He leaned over to Jeremy: "Hey, Jez! They thought that was Robert! The mix-up over Joseph is priceless! Let's see if we can keep this going, it's hilarious!" Jeremy smiled and nodded his assent.

"Where are you lot from, why are you all so weird and what the hell was all that about? Whoever's heard of a bloke needing help get his thingy out?" Jackie asked, with a look of serious concern and alarm.

Melanie, meanwhile, was standing next to her with her hand over her mouth, so it was hard to tell if she was horrified or laughing her socks off.

Jeremy tried to explain and did a superb job of keeping a straight face.

"We're from Leicestershire and we're walking the Cleveland Way, camping as we go. Tonight we're stopping at the Saltwick Caravan Park on the way through to Filey, which we should reach by Wednesday, unless, of course, you invite us to stay here for a night or two of passion, in which case we don't mind staying till the weekend!"

Luckily the girls missed the last line, because at that moment Robert returned with the relieved look of someone who has successfully done what a man has to do, with or without his Joseph getting a helping hand. His entrance somehow diverted the attention of the two young ladies from trying to understand what was going on.

Jackie was the most forthcoming and confident of the pair and immediately asked some pertinent questions, which Robert, in all innocence, answered to the best of his ability.

"How's Joseph now then?" she snapped, sternly and severely.

"Very happy now, thank you very much for asking! Bit of a weight off his mind, I can tell you!"

Jackie continued, somewhat perturbed. "Not shrivelled or hiding away then? I mean, you obviously needed a hand with things!"

"No, not shrivelled at all, thankfully. You can't beat getting a hand though, if you're free later on," Robert replied.

Jeremy could see things were getting out of hand. He decided to step in.

"Chris, why don't you get a round of drinks?" He handed Chris a couple of pound notes and then asked Robert to join him outside. Ever up for a free drink, the canny northern girls turned on the charm and placed an order for their entire group, which Chris, having received a wink from Jeremy, played along with.

Robert, meanwhile, reluctantly followed Jeremy outside. "What's up Jeremy? I'm doing really well in there! What have you dragged me out here for?"

Jeremy explained. "It's Joseph, he's been dropped by Yvonne and won't come out of the phone box. Martin wants you to have a go."

The two of them walked over the street to the phone box. The first thing Jeremy did was despatch Martin back to the bar.

"Martin, go and ask the girls we were with to help you get Joe out, I'm sure they won't mind. They seem really nice!" Jeremy was determined to give the case of mistaken identity more potential to expand.

Martin needed no second bidding. Secretly, he'd been quite jealous to find his friends engaged in conversation with some lovely Whitby girls. This was a perfect chance to leave Robert to deal with Joseph and for him to look the caring hero with the ladies. He raced into the bar in time to find the four females joining their table with the round of drinks Chris had just purchased.

"Would one of you ladies like to help me with a problem please?"

"Don't tell me your little chum needs a hand again!" said a cheerful, but guarded, Melanie.

"Yes, he's in a right mess this time. I'm still desperate to get him out. I'm sure you'll all love Joseph when you get to meet him. I just know one of you will get him to stand up again. He's been sulking for ages!"

Jackie was horrified. "Is there somebody looking after you? I mean there has to be a screw loose somewhere! Have you no shame! Can't you stop talking about your bloody... well... bloody Joseph!"

Martin was taken aback. The conversation wasn't flowing in the right direction at all. It was sort of flowing, but it was as if something had been badly misunderstood by one or both of them and why was this beautiful girl being so aggressive?

"No, no, you don't understand. I'm honestly worried about Joseph. I've never seen him so browbeaten and low. He needs some TLC, the type of TLC only a beautiful lady like you can provide."

To be fair, Jackie had drunk most of the rum and coke Chris

had just plied her with. However, it still came as quite a shock to Martin when he received the balance straight in his face! At that moment, Martin realised he would never fully understand the workings of the female mind for as long as he lived!

The incident was saved from escalation by the miraculous appearance of Andrew, Andreas, Jeremy – the real Joseph – and, of course, Robert.

"Bloody hell, there's two of the weird pillocks!" Jackie announced loudly.

Jeremy made a poignant introduction. "Melanie, Jackie, Caroline, err… Mrs Melanie, I would like you to meet Joseph and, of course, the other twin brother! There's been a few mix-ups tonight, which frankly, only Chris and I knew about, but it was worth it 'cos it's been the funniest night out we've ever had!"

The full significance of the confusion slowly revealed itself. Gradually everything came good, except for Joseph who had to carry the scar of recent rejection. Robert purchased him a rum and coke, the first of several Joe downed that evening. Not being a drinker, these soon took effect and he became somewhat intoxicated. All of the walkers took turns trying to console him in an attempt to help him get over his failed relationship.

In the bar, the three younger ladies chatted and flirted until late with all the other hikers. Andrew noticed the girl's mother on the sidelines and decided to make conversation.

"Have you lived in Whitby long?" Andrew enquired.

"Yes."

"Do you work?"

"No."

"Are you married?"

"Yes."

"What does your husband do?" Andrew was nothing if not persistent.

"Smokes kippers."

"Don't you let him near the cigarettes?"

Silence.

"Do you have any hobbies?" Andrew made a last-ditch attempt at conversation.

"Well, I've got me cigarettes."

At this point, Andrew made an excuse and joined the others. In all fairness, he had tried!

At about 10.30pm, the ladies simply moved on, leaving the seven to finish their drinks. All dreams of sexual conquest evaporated and instead became civilised goodbyes, although Robert did manage a lingering snog with the birthday girl. The only damper on the evening was Joseph, who by now was slightly unwell.

"Come on, let's head home," Andrew suggested. "We're going to have to go steady with Joseph and tomorrow we've got to get up and off to Robin Hood's Bay."

The walk up the 199 steps seemed to take forever with Joseph being supported by various members of the group. On Abbey Lane, Joseph decided to relinquish the tenuous hold on his cod and chip supper. After an eternity of retching, during which time Joseph renewed his acquaintance with the hymn 'All Things Bright and Beautiful', which to the other six seemed an unusual song to sing while vomiting in the hedge bottom, he finally recovered enough to allow them all to continue back to their tents.

Nobody was surprised when Martin made Joseph sleep with his head out of the tent, just in case, so to speak! However, the night passed without incident and six hikers awoke on Easter Monday full of enthusiasm for the walk between Whitby and

Robin Hood's Bay. The seventh, Joseph, woke with both head-ache and heartache. Only the former would get better as the day progressed. The latter would take much longer to dissipate.

Chapter 14

Whitby to Robin Hood's Bay

Easter Monday saw another slow start, not surprising as it was a sort of 'morning after the night before' type of morning. Admittedly, only Joseph was really the worse for wear and it showed. He looked miserable. The loss of Yvonne was an event that was to haunt him for the rest of his life.

The day was a fine one, but windy. Actually, you'd call it bracing and just the sort of weather to blow the cobwebs away. Breakfast was a gentle affair as it was realised that today's walk was a relatively short one. A walk to be savoured, where there was time to take in the scenery, read up on the places of interest and explore the seaside village of Robin Hood's Bay. The only chore was going to be keeping Joseph's spirits up. Conversation, when Joseph wasn't in earshot, centred on how they were going to prevent him from leaping off a cliff or dwelling too much on his miserable position. The result was a co-ordinated effort to ensure he was watched at all times and continually engaged in cheerful conversation wherever possible.

Naturally, Joseph was off his food. Naturally, Joseph was quiet and subdued. Naturally, the other walkers were supportive – up to a point – and naturally, Joseph was totally at a loss as to why Yvonne had given him the old heave-ho.

"I should never have come on this walk. She said she didn't want me to come, I should have listened and stayed with her this Easter. I feel like part of me is missing, like someone's thrust a knife into my very soul." (At this point, Jeremy was thinking what he really needed was a kick up the ar-soul.) Joseph announced that, instead of walking, he felt like hiding away and writing poetry, or sitting on a hilltop singing to himself.

Out of nowhere, he put his feelings directly into song and, to the embarrassed amazement of the group, gave a slightly tuneless rendition of the opening stanzas of the Carpenters' song 'Goodbye to Love':

"I'll say goodbye to love,
No one ever cared if I should live or die.
Time and time again the chance
For love has passed me by
And all I know of love
Is how to live without it,
I just can't seem to find it.
So I've made up my mind I must
Live my life alone...."

"Oh no, I've forgotten the words! Come on fellas, how does it go on?"

Robert summed up everyone's feelings: "Thank Christ for that! Cheer up, Joseph, for crying out loud. If you're going to be like this for the rest of the day – or the rest of the walk – we're all going to go mad!"

An indignant Joseph was unrepentant. "It's all right for you, Robert, you seem immune to the emotional side of love. I mean, you've got a girlfriend who you didn't even bother to ring last night! Instead, you ended up snogging that girl in the pub! How can you do that when you have Ruth waiting for you back in the 'Vale'? You need to get in touch with God again and find some compassion."

"Carry on like this, Joseph, and we'll put you permanently in touch with God!" muttered Robert, not maliciously, but in an attempt to find humour in the situation.

Chris was the only member of the group to acknowledge the humour in Robert's statement by openly laughing out loud. For his efforts, he received an incredulous stare from everybody, bar Robert.

Martin became peacemaker and went over to help Joe with packing his rucksack. He also provided a listening ear as Joe began to recount all the lovely times he had spent with Yvonne before bursting into tears at the realisation those lovely times were, indeed, over.

Watching from a distance, Jeremy leaned over to Andrew. "You know today is supposed to be only a short walk, but I've a feeling it's going to turn into a flaming long day, especially if Joe is going to carry on like this!"

"It's not today I'm worried about, Jez, it's the rest of the walk! Somehow we've got to snap him out of it!" Andrew replied.

After making full use of the facilities on offer at the Saltwick Caravan Park and after paying their dues, the hikers set off on yet another coastal trek. Not long after leaving the camping ground, the Cleveland Way passed close to the Whitby Bull, a fog signal station, just beyond which was the lighthouse at Whitestone Point. Here the wind became much stronger and whipped up spume from the ocean, blowing it up over their heads and inland. The experience of walking along the cliff edge with strong winds blowing in from the sea added greatly to the exhilaration of this section of the walk.

Joseph seemed to settle down, although this may have been an illusion. One fortuitous consequence of the windy conditions was the prevention of conversation between people strung out in a line, unless a deliberate effort was made. The deliberate effort being to turn right around so as to direct the soundwaves emanating from the mouth straight into the ears of whoever was being addressed.

However for Martin, walking behind Joseph, and for Jeremy, walking directly in front of him, it was disconcerting to hear snippets of Joe's heartfelt attempt to sing Bill Withers' song 'Ain't No Sunshine':

"Ain't no sunshine when she's gone
It's not warm when she's away
And she's always gone too long every time she goes away."

Nobody else could hear his faltering attempts, so all Martin and Jeremy could reasonably do was keep walking and watch closely for signs of him leaping to an untimely death over the cliff to their left. Martin couldn't help but think that, while walking the Cleveland Way was an uplifting and marvellous thing to do, doing it with someone even remotely suicidal probably wasn't very clever, as there existed ample opportunity to end it all!

At Hawsker Bottoms, the Oakham Beck crossed the walking track only to descend over a cliff to Maw Wyke Hole. Amazingly, the waterfall had turned into a 'water rise' as the wind whipped the falling water back upwards again. At this point, the hikers had to run the gauntlet of a vertical shower of stream water. Robert addressed those around him, which fortunately didn't include Joe!

"Maybe a face full of cold water is what Joseph needs to snap him out of it!"

It didn't work though, it had completely the opposite effect. The next song Martin and Jeremy caught snippets of was Buddy Holly's 'Raining in my Heart':

"The sun is out, the sky is blue
There's not a cloud to spoil the view
But it's raining. Raining in my heart."

Martin and Jeremy decided not to ignore it this time and joined in with gusto!

"The weather man says clear today
He doesn't know you've gone away
And it's raining. Raining in my heart"

By now the well-known tune had passed up and down the line until everyone who knew it was able to join in. The most appropriate lines were then sung at maximum volume out across the North Sea. The Whitby Bull fog signal would have been pushed to make more noise!

"Oh misery! mis… er… re… ee… ee… eey
What's going to become of me?"

Chris wasn't alone in laughing inappropriately this time as everybody, bar Joe, saw the funny side and laughed out loud.

Joseph just shut up and walked quietly – for a while!

Further on below Raindale came an unexpected treat that stopped the entire group in its tracks. Even Joseph momentarily forgot his woes, as an unbelievable display by jackdaws – of all things – took centre stage. The wind from the sea was blasting against the steep sides of Far Jetticks, the semi-circular bay below Raindale. Several dozen jackdaws had found the natural air curtain that was being directed sharply upward by the angle of the cliffs. The birds were flying high and then folding their wings before plummeting down the cliff at enormous speed, only to ascend again. In short, they were having as much fun as a group of children repeatedly getting rides on a fairground roller coaster! Just for once, Andrew didn't need to cajole the walkers to enjoy birdwatching. They were that enthused that lunch was brought forward and eaten watching daredevil groups of these grey-headed crows hooning about the sky, having the time of their lives.

Martin summed up the feeling shared by all when he said: "You don't need to watch nature programmes on television, filmed in some foreign country, to realise how exciting the natural world is. You just have to get out and see something like this!"

The walk then continued around the cliffs, until the magnificent view of Robin Hood's Bay opened up. In no time at all, the hikers were entering the outskirts.

"There's a campsite to the north, just up there," said Robert, pointing up the B1447 that lead away from the village.

"Perhaps we had better go and find a camping spot now and then we can explore Robin Hood's Bay without our backpacks?"

No one took much convincing, as memories of how pleasant it had been exploring Whitby minus rucksacks, were fresh in their minds.

Yet again, pleasant campsite owners allowed seven grubby young men the privilege of using their facilities. Yet again, those facilities were well utilised, but by now it was almost too late to make any difference. This was, after all, the penultimate night of their adventure. Only two more nights camping and they could sleep in their own beds again!

Mid-afternoon saw all the tents erected and airing beautifully in the windy conditions. Time was taken to wash socks and undies and hang them on the clothes line provided by the camp ground owners. A meeting of minds was held to sort out the remaining food, of which, fortunately, there wasn't much. It was decided to eat out in Robin Hood's Bay that evening, leaving cereals, dried milk, sugar, eggs, bacon, cheese, biscuits, apples and a loaf of bread for the rest of the trip. It was assumed a campsite would be obtainable in Scarborough and that the last night would include a meal out in some comfort. This was to prove a serious error of judgement!

With equipment sorted for the next day and grubby bodies cleaned up as best they could be, the seven walkers descended into the old part of Robin Hood's Bay village. Here again was a quaint seaside settlement, with loads of history and fantastic views across the bay. The Cleveland Way book by Bill Cowley didn't enlighten the walkers much, but they found the old village and the stout sea wall, which appeared to hold the buildings in place against a pounding sea, an interesting place to wander round in the few hours available at the end of Easter Monday.

Tea consisted of a variety of pastries purchased from a small bakery and included Yorkshire tea cakes. These were eaten sitting at the bottom of the town, overlooking the bay. It had been realised earlier that tomorrow's walk to Scarborough wouldn't pass through any settlements with shops, so Jeremy purchased a few extras for lunch and everyone stocked up on chocolate bars again.

While the group were busy buying and eating, Joseph seemed to forget his woes. However, sitting on the sea wall and admiring the view set him off again. His heartfelt wish was that Yvonne could be there with them all to admire the view and for her to realise how lovely the walk was and how she should have been pleased he had taken part. Jeremy could see he was brooding again and is if to interpret the mood began to sing. He was joined by almost everyone when he kicked off with the Everly Brothers' version of 'Bye Bye Love':

"Bye bye love
Bye bye sweet caress
Hello emptiness
I feel like I could die
Bye bye my love goodbye."

Then Joseph joined in, so things were looking up!

Before departing from Robin Hood's Bay and heading for an early night, Robert suggested they have at least one drink in the pub down near the sea. This turned out to be an unsuccessful venture in a most unusual way. Robert led the way to the bar and placed an order for several drinks. The barman accepted his order but, casting his eye over the group, hesitated when he caught sight of Robert's twin brother Martin.

"How old are you then, you don't look eighteen?" The barman asked.

"I'm the same age as him!" Martin said, pointing at his brother.

This time the bar man addressed Robert. "So, how old are you?"

"Well, near enough 18. We won't say anything if you won't!" Robert replied flippantly.

The barman stopped pouring and gave the walkers the once over, once again.

"Sorry, lads, come back in a years' time! It's more than me

job's worth to serve you. Sorry."

Dejectedly, the hikers left the pub. Immediately on entering the street, Robert turned on Martin.

"Well done, Martin, you could try and look more mature. You're pathetic!"

With that, Martin took several swings at Robert and this time made a rare connection, sending Robert flying into the side of a building. Before he could retaliate, the full force of the peacekeeping militia grabbed him and held him back. Andreas was left to restrain a very emotional and perturbed Martin, who was most indignant at being held responsible for them not being served alcohol. To one side stood Chris, bent double laughing again – much to the disapproval of everybody!

A subdued bunch of hikers left the shoreline of Robin Hood's Bay for the return journey to the campsite. Joseph was quiet and depressed again, Robert was being held at the back in case he retaliated against Martin's outburst, and Martin was vocally abusive and agitated, not just at his brother, but at the 'short-sighted, stupid barman' for picking him out of the crowd when he looked just like his twin.

It had been a peculiar day on the Cleveland Way. Not a particularly hard day's work physically, but somewhat emotionally draining for almost everybody. Tomorrow was a much longer walk – a real challenge, in fact, and being the penultimate day, the smell of a profound victory over the 'Cleveland Way' was in the air.

Roll on Tuesday. Bring it on!

Chapter 15

Robin Hood's Bay to Scarborough

Andreas woke early on Tuesday morning. With him shuffling around in the tent getting dressed, it went without saying that Chris and Andrew were awake too. Once Chris and Andrew began getting dressed and unzipping the tent door, then those in the other two tents began to stir. By 8am, everybody was up and at it and following the well-rehearsed routine of ablutions, breakfast, tent dismantling and rucksack packing. By 9am, they were off, back down the hill into Robin Hood's Bay.

"Remember what I said about what goes down must go up again?" asked Jeremy with a note of sarcasm in his voice.

"Yes, what about it, Jez?" asked Andrew innocently.

"Well, Andy, keep your wits about ya, 'cos I reckon that it's happening again!"

Jeremy wasn't wrong. Heading south-east out of the village, almost from the very bottom of the street where the sea meets the jetty, the track began to climb again up on to the low, almost muddy, cliffs that form the landward edge of Robin Hood's Bay.

Straight away it became apparent that this section of coast was suffering more than its share of erosion and, judging by the loose consistency of the cliffs, it wasn't hard to imagine why the sea found it so easy to make inroads into the landscape. Signs of land slippage could be seen on the way up the path and looking back down towards the sea.

The day was not as clear as yesterday and at times a light drizzle added some moisture. At Boggle Hole, after descending back to sea level and before climbing yet again, the entire group stopped to put on wet-weather gear. The walk was quiet and peaceful. It passed over attractive farmland with the sounds of the sea over to the left-hand side.

A mile or so later, the track entered a disturbed area now being reclaimed by nature. The quarries were once a large alum works that, according to Bill Cowley's book, were used well into the nineteenth century. Just past these quarries, appearing through the mist was a golf course, which, despite the early hour and light rain, had a couple of pairs of golfers wandering across it. The course, built on the side of a gentle hill, was the preserve of patrons of the large, majestic hotel now mysteriously manifesting itself high above the walkers. The hotel dominated the landscape and its isolated position was immediately attractive to Andrew.

The Cleveland Way skirted the edge of the course, leading the walkers inland. A quick check with Robert showed clearly that after the hotel the track reasserted its right to pass along the cliff top. This aristocratic monolith of a hotel had clearly been the cause of the walking track's diversion and as such became even more appealing to Andrew.

Upon reaching the driveway to the establishment and on reading the impressive signage 'The Raven Hall Hotel', Andrew made a solemn promise to himself. He didn't let anyone else know of this, keeping it firmly secret. His vow was to one day return with enough money to stay at this wonderful looking establishment!

Nobody else seemed particularly moved by the place, or by the unique layout and history of the unusual settlement of Ravenscar. No one noticed the old disused railway line from

Scarborough to Whitby, which was built to go through a tunnel alongside the Raven Hall Hotel to appease its owners, just so they wouldn't have to look at it! No wonder the Cleveland Way had been diverted around its imposing structure and grounds!

The end of the Cleveland Way was uppermost in the minds of all the hikers. The walk had now become something to be defeated. The glory of completing one of the United Kingdom's longest overland hikes was beckoning and it started to dominate the thoughts and actions of the walkers. The end at Filey wasn't all that far away. Returning home to a hero's welcome infiltrated the minds of all seven young men and kept one leg passing the other in monotonous regularity. They were tired, but could keep going because their bodies had grown used to the daily routine. In fact, the more they walked, the more they could walk. The more the heavy rucksacks pressed down on tired vertebrae, the more stiff backs were able to resist. The only thing proving irritating today was Joseph, yet again!

He was still heartbroken. Not quite as bad as yesterday, but if left alone with anyone, Joseph would begin to reminisce and then bemoan his loss. At lunch time, among some old Second World War observation buildings just past Ravenscar, Jeremy was eating and trying not to listen as Joseph was trying to convince Martin to ring Yvonne. Joseph wanted Martin to tell her how she should give him another chance, how she had failed to realise just how sincere his love was for her. Part of this grand plan for reconnection was for Martin to convince Yvonne that he was deeply worried for Joseph and that she should at least phone him. Joseph would, he reasoned, pick up the pieces from there!

Jeremy caught the eye of several of the other hikers, who were eavesdropping on this conversation as well. Jeremy just did what he did best and took the mickey by singing! Out of nowhere, he gave a powerful rendition of Harry Nilsson's classic 'Without You'! The song was taken up by everyone yet again, but this time in exaggerated and very humorous form. A pack of hounds would have sounded better:

"I can't live if living is without you who-who
I can't live, I can't give any more... or... or... or
I can't live if living is without you boohoo
I can't give, I can't give any more or... or... or."

Joseph didn't talk much about Yvonne after that – not to any of the hikers anyway!

After lunch, the weather improved slightly, clearing enough for Andrew to see another new bird in a field near Beast Cliff, not far from Staintondale. The bird was a yellow wagtail. Martin showed the most interest – actually Martin was the only one to show any interest, even going so far as to borrow Andrew's binoculars to view the half dozen birds flitting alongside the walkers.

"Aren't they the same as we saw near Rievaulx Abbey? You know, on the rocks by the river?"

"No, Martin, they were grey wagtails! There's quite a difference, these migrate for a start and are much less common! Actually, we're quite lucky to see them," Andrew explained, before they both had to labour to catch up with everybody again.

Soon afterwards the route took them down into the wooded valley of Hayburn Wyke. Another break used up more time than expected and was indicative of the general tiredness over-coming the hikers. Upwards and onwards saw them climb out of this beautiful valley and back on to the scenic cliff walk to the east of Burniston. After yet more downs and ups and some interesting circumnavigations around inlets and headlands, the town of Scarborough began to come into view.

By now it was late and the first evidence of dusk began to appear. Andrew began to get concerned and called for an update from Robert and a check on campsites marked on the map.

"Well, Rob, can you see any campsites marked this side of Scarborough? If there are any we should divert now and get sorted for the night. I don't know about you lot, but a hot shower would go down well at the moment."

Robert found a campsite on Burniston Road, which looked like the only one on the northern side of Scarborough. Nobody wanted to walk right through the town looking for a site, so a diversion was made off to the west and away from the clifftop.

Straight away the campsite looked posh. It was immaculate. There were no tents anywhere, only caravans that looked like they had all mod cons and were towed by brand new cars. Joseph was immediately concerned about cost, but by now it was getting dark and all seven were seriously tired.

The motley group walked up to the reception and received an ominous glare from an elderly couple walking away from the building. The seven never even made it into the reception area. Instead, the owner hurried out to meet them. He was an older gentleman who quite obviously had the status of his upmarket caravan park uppermost in his mind. He just stood at the reception door, looked the hikers up and down and sent them packing with their tails between their legs:

"No, no, sorry lads, I don't think so. No, I really don't think so!"

That's all he said. He didn't get a reply or a single question from any of the walkers. All together they turned and, without uttering a word, walked away! In all fairness, the seven walkers weren't suitable for that type of establishment. In all fairness, they were filthy, bedraggled and smelly. In short, they looked like ruffians of the worst sort and on reflection nobody held it against the owner for refusing them admission. They still needed somewhere to camp though!

Outside the campsite grounds, an emergency meeting was convened. Nobody wanted to carry on walking – everyone had had quite enough for one day.

"But there's no campsite this end of Scarborough!" Robert reminded them urgently.

"Right, let's walk back towards the Cleveland Way alongside this river," said Chris, who had been studying the map. "Maybe we will get lucky and find some waste ground, or something. After all, it's getting dark, so if we hide away a bit then leave early in the morning before folks get around, we'll be OK?"

Chris phrased this more as a question than a statement of intent, but by this time only one person had the energy to argue.

Andrew wasn't happy at the prospect: "If we camp here, that puts paid to us going into Scarborough tonight, to eat or anything else, because we will have to guard our gear – you know our tents and stuff. Not only that, but one day when I was off school sick I watched this programme on Scarborough. The police have loads of trouble with folks just pitching tents any old place. I reckon they would take a dim view of us just pitching without permission!"

Andrew was outvoted and a dispirited group made its way down the small track past Scalby Mills alongside Scalby Beck. In faded light, a suitable spot was located well out of sight of houses and passing traffic. The land was obviously not farmed as the fences were nothing special and there was no evidence of grazing. There was rubbish lying around though, so it wasn't exactly pristine or salubrious. After picking some flat ground and pitching tents, an assessment was made of food and drink reserves. Jeremy had a firm grasp on what commodities remained and by pooling all their water bottles it became apparent they had enough to scrape by for one night.

"Right, we're going to have a fry-up!" announced Jeremy. "Then there's cheese, apples and biscuits."

"Yum, yum, yum!" said Chris sarcastically.

Joseph was concerned about breakfast. "What about tomorrow, Jez? Have we anything for breakfast?"

"We've got dried milk, so if we leave enough water we'll be alright for cereal. After that it's just more cheese and apples!" an unusually cheerful Jeremy replied.

"It doesn't matter about tomorrow though, does it? I mean it's the last day! We start by walking round the edge of Scarborough, so we can buy something then surely?" Andrew announced. Secretly, Andrew was of the opinion they were all too filthy to be going in any shop, especially considering the response from the caravan park owner earlier.

Andrew continued to address the group: "Look, I'm really worried about this police thing. I'm going to find a phone box and ring my dad. It'll give me chance to confirm with him that we will make Filey tomorrow. I don't know about you lot, but I'm ready for home, especially after tonight's setback! What I'll also do is get him to phone Scarborough police and explain where we are and just say that we had no choice – we just ran out of time. That way, if they do find us at least they know a bit about us. It might make things better!"

Unusually, no one objected and Martin even agreed to accompany Andrew. Robert provided a map reference, in case the police really wanted to find the group. A short walk into the outskirts of Scarborough soon located a telephone box. During his conversation with Andrew, Mike Price agreed to have a chat with the Scarborough police. He also agreed to meet the walkers at around 3.30pm at Filey Brigg car park the following day.

In no time at all, Andrew and Martin were back at the campsite sharing the group's 'last supper'. There was precious little water available to wash utensils properly, certainly not enough to allow a thorough wash of themselves. Not that it really mattered as their clothes were grubby anyway.

Everyone retired to bed feeling uncomfortable, dirty and strangely threatened and unsafe. The night spent on Hasty Bank hadn't engendered the same feelings of insecurity at all. The proximity to Scarborough hadn't lent any feelings of security – quite the opposite. In short, fear of other humans was far more unsettling than fear of the wilderness.

Behind the scenes, Mike Price had indeed telephoned Scarborough police to explain the predicament faced by the seven hikers. The kindly policeman who spoke with him that night reassured Mike that they turned a blind eye to one-off, overnight, campers. He noted the map reference and put Mike's mind at ease, telling him that the location of their camp was fairly well hidden and that they should survive the night in one piece!

Despite being in desperate need of a good night's sleep, everyone slept badly with frequent toilet visits necessitating a walk into a cold, drizzly night. Only the prospect of the imagined victorious last day's walk and of their own comfy beds at home kept spirits from flagging. Oh, and home cooking of course, especially considering that the night's meal hadn't been one of their best!

Chapter 16

Scarborough to Filey

Naturally, it was Andreas who led the attack on the final day, just as he had done on most of the others. That morning, though, nobody complained as everyone stirred with a common purpose.

Joseph had woken with thoughts of his mock A-level English exam. Emerging from his tent, he decided to test his memory for one of his favourite poems by A.E. Housman. As he stood upright, he addressed the group after adopting his familiar actor's stance:

"Yonder see the morning blink:
The sun is up, and up must I,
To wash and dress and eat and drink
And look at things and talk and think
And work, and God knows why.
Oh often have I washed and dressed
And what's to show for all my pain?
Let me abed and rest:
Ten thousand times I've done my best
And all's to do again."

This was followed by a flowery bow and subdued clapping from the one or two who had bothered to take in Joseph's profound words of wisdom. He realised he had 'died on stage' and that he wasn't going to change anything with poetry today, so he simply got on with his morning routine!

The weather had turned cold and damp. It wasn't raining hard, but the drizzle meant that the flysheets on the tents were covered in fine droplets of water. Breakfast finally saw all the cereal eaten, with the most watery, reconstituted milk consumed on the walk. The dried milk powder was supposed to be skimmed, but what was mixed today couldn't even be classed as that! Just describing it as white was an exaggeration.

There was no water for washing or cleaning teeth. No one could face going to the loo in the drizzle so it was decided that the first public toilets encountered on the walk around Scarborough sea front would be commandeered by the walkers for ablutions *en masse*. Gradually the camp was dismantled and damp tents squirreled away into the backpacks for the last time. Finally, they were ready for departure. Andrew gave the site his customary once over for litter before the walkers formed up for the final day's assault. A track led off down the northern side of Scalby Beck in the direction of the sea. With purposeful strides, the seven broke camp for the final time on their Cleveland Way adventure.

Soon after rejoining the official walking route and after crossing Scalby Beck, they found themselves on the Scarborough seafront running along North Bay. Just before Marine Drive they located what they had been looking for – a typical seaside toilet block with several cubicles and a row of large porcelain sinks. An opportunity to clean themselves up a bit presented itself and at this early time of the day they had the place to themselves. Naturally, there was no hot water, but despite this luxury being absent, most of the seven stripped to the waist and had stand-up baths.

Feeling fresh from washing and shaving, the hikers

continued around Castle Hill, passing the silent attractions of Luna Park and onwards along the edge of the old harbour. It was unusual to experience a seaside resort such as Scarborough so deserted. Most of the seven had been to Scarborough with their parents at some point in their lives, usually on day trips and always during the busy summer period. On these trips the seafront was packed with families walking on the promenade, riding the donkeys on the beach, or spending loose change in the penny arcades. Today though, there were very few people about. The busy amusement arcades were closed and almost all the cafés and souvenir shops were still locked up.

Alongside the old harbour, the seven split up with Andrew, Martin, Chris and Robert staying next to the sea and the rest remaining on the other side of the road. Andrew was the instigator of the split as he had spotted small groups of turnstones – small wading birds usually seen on rocky beaches – actually wandering around on the pavement. Such was Andrew's excitement that several of the group went with him to get a closer look.

Naturally, the two separate groups engaged in some banter across the road, resulting in Martin becoming so engrossed in verbally abusing Andreas that he walked head first into a lamp post, knocking himself to the ground! Andrew and Robert immediately ran to his aid as he really had hit the post with some force. Those on the other side of the street also ran over to lend assistance. Chris, on the other hand, was laughing so energetically, he had to sit down to allow his body to double over. Robert was not impressed at all. Despite all the fights between the twins, when the chips were down, they were genuinely protective of one another. On this occasion, Chris became the recipient of the full force of Robert's verbal fury. Robert called him all the names under the sun. He admonished him for his lousy sense of humour and for always laughing at inappropriate things. Frankly, Chris was lucky not to receive a punch, such was Robert's angst. Meanwhile, in the background, Martin was recovering but the incident left him with a headache for the rest of the day!

Chris was apologetic and for a while subdued. He actually seemed to take on board Robert's comments as if some turning point had been reached. Most notably, from that day forward, he was never quite as blatantly amused by his friend's misfortunes!

Halfway along Foreshore Road, the walkers found a small shop selling ready-made sandwiches and confectionery. Jeremy was able to use the last of the kitty buying food for lunch. The seven hikers then descended on to South Sands to complete their walk around South Bay. With Scarborough Castle behind them up on Castle Hill and the splendour of the Grand Hotel on the right-hand side in front of them, the scenery appeared in complete contrast to the wild cliff tops and moorland they had been walking through during the last nine days. A few more people were beginning to emerge, walking along the foreshore and on the beach. Several older men were already on the sand digging for lugworms, obviously with the intention of going fishing.

The Cleveland Way track was properly regained at the end of South Bay promenade above the sea bathing pool. For the next few miles, the walk twisted and turned along low cliffs, firstly next to Cornelian Bay and then Cayton Bay. The seven walkers were concentrating hard on the final few miles of the expedition. Despite the proximity of civilisation and the noise from the main A165 near Cayton Bay, the coastal views were still stimulating and the undulating track still challenging enough to make this section of the hike no walk in the park.

Beyond Lebberston Cliff the track passed in front of a series of caravan parks. From beneath, on Castle and Casty Rocks, strange bellowing noises could be heard, unlike anything the walkers had ever experienced. A halt was called to investigate and the answer was provided by Andrew, who was able to see seals hauled out on the rocks below. These animals were making an incredible racket calling to each other. So much time was spent passing around the binoculars to get a glimpse of these creatures that Jeremy decided to make it an official lunch break. Sandwiches were eaten on the edge of a caravan park gazing down on, what were for the seven Leicestershire residents, very unusual animals indeed.

The end of the expedition was getting close and a feeling of excitement began to grip the hikers. During the last mile or so, the 'band members' led the group in song. Martin began by singing 'Oh Boy'. This was followed by everyone belting out 'When the Saints Go Marching In'. Spirits were high as the walkers descended towards Filey Brigg.

"We've done it! We've walked the Cleveland Way!" an expansive and obviously excited Chris announced to the group as they approached the finish line. Chris led the walkers in celebratory back slaps and insisted on taking a photo as the hikers walked towards Filey. Just for the record, Andrew took a picture of Chris posing as the all-conquering explorer in his orange wet-weather gear before reaching the car park where Mike Price was due to pick them up.

As the car park came into view, the familiar shape of Mike's Transit van appeared. Their timing had been spot on, it was three o'clock. Mike was waiting with the rear doors wide open. He greeted all seven walkers with a handshake and hearty congratulations. Then he pointed to the flasks of tea and slices of cake waiting just inside the back of the van, which the hikers fell on with relish.

"Well, come on then, tell me the high points!" Mike urged as the walkers gathered around with refreshments in hand.

Andrew was quickly in. "Well, Roseberry Topping was definitely the high point for me!"

This was met with the usual groans and mutterings to which Andrew had become accustomed and it was left to Jeremy to explain to Mike what all the fuss was about.

Jeremy then went on to describe his highlight, which turned out to be the vicar's garage in Great Ayton: "That garage meant so much to me. We were cold and soaked through. I really didn't want to spend another night in a tent and I needed somewhere to spread my wet clothes. It was really good of that vicar to let us use it and I remember lying there thinking how grateful I was to be out of the weather, even though the floor was so hard!"

Andreas was next to voice his feelings. "Until this week we've only really known each other at school, but for the past ten days or so we've been surviving together, which has been great. A completely new experience with no adult supervision – brilliant – and I'm so glad we did it! The singing was fun and thinking about it now, that Jimmy Osmond mix-up with the jukebox in Staithes was hilarious!"

Chris was next to jump in with his take on the adventure. "I enjoyed the planning as much as the walk. We've had some great laughs like at Whitby and the Holly Bush Hotel in Skelton. The walks in the wild weather on the moors were fantastic and I've enjoyed being with all of you, despite none of you understanding my unique and wonderful sense of humour!"

Robert was next to add his thoughts. "Like Jeremy, the vicar's garage meant a lot. It was just a stone-floored shed really, but we were really glad of it because we didn't know where else we would be. The challenge of map reading and the wild weather on the moors was exhilarating. That camp at Hasty Bank on the moors when we gathered in the little sheep shed drinking hot tea and listening to funny stories takes some beating as well."

"Don't forget the snipe drumming overhead!" added Andrew.

"The snipe was unusual and the other birds were interesting too," Martin said as he revealed his memorable moments. "For me, it's been the biggest thing I've done so far in my life. I imagine this is how real explorers feel after they've completed some epic adventure! We've had loads of laughs, some hard walks in shocking weather, but also some lovely days with beautiful views. I, for one, will never forget this walk and for me the Yorkshire Moors will always be somewhere very special."

Martin's words were met with vocal approval from everyone present.

"What about you Joseph? You haven't had your penny's worth yet!" Mike enquired, as all eyes turned to the poetic wordsmith the walkers had all got to know so intimately over the last ten days.

"Well, you don't know it, Mr Price, but my girlfriend, Yvonne, ditched me three-quarters of the way through the walk. That's added a sad dimension to the whole thing for me, I must say, but overall, I reckon it's been an adventure that's made me aware that something deeply moving has occurred for all of us. Now and again we've squabbled, but camaraderie has shone through. We've pulled together and overcome adversity, we've had a chance to reflect on life and a chance to find out about each other. We're just a bunch of ordinary

Leicestershire youths who've made for ourselves an extraordinary adventure! We've had a memorable experience that I will always remember and cherish for the rest of my life. We didn't have to travel to some exotic, distant shore. We didn't have to spend a fortune either and we've learnt so much more about England and each other. Fantastic!"

Finally, Andrew added his thanks to his father for not only suggesting the Cleveland Way in the first place, but for going out of his way to transport all the walkers to Helmsley at the start and now retrieving them all from Filey at the end. The thanks were warmly echoed by all the others in the group.

After half an hour or so of excited chatter and refreshment, the van was finally loaded with rucksacks and young men. The very first thing Mike Price did was open the van windows, which is where they stayed for the entire journey home to Leicestershire. Putting it bluntly, the hikers stunk to high heaven. Despite their efforts in the Scarborough toilet block, ten days of walking, combined with rain, mud and sweat, had left its mark and frankly, all seven were in dire need of a shower and clean clothes.

The ride home was strangely quiet and subdued. The walkers were no longer in control of their destiny. They were heading home to continue where they had left off. It was a peculiar transition from the thrill of the hike to the confines of civilisation. All seven were tired, but all were thinking about what was next in their lives.

One by one, Mike Price dropped off the hikers at their homes. One by one, the individuals faced their families – some asked lots of questions, some asked none. They were all grateful for baths, showers, washing machines, home-cooked meals and family. But, all seven felt a strong feeling of anti-climax in the days that followed, caused by the impossibility of describing to others the full glory of what they had experienced during those few memorable days in April 1974.

In short, the entire ten days proved to be an hilarious masterpiece of youthful exuberance. The desire to 'have a laugh' had been well and truly achieved.

Postscript

This book was written forty years after the seven hikers had completed their walk.

Eighty-five per cent of what is written here actually occurred, so only a few small embellishments have been made!

All seven participants still have fond memories of the expedition and all agree the event occurred at a major crossroads in their lives – just as Joseph had predicted.

Joseph went to university, studied history and became a teacher and theologian in the Midlands. He is married and has a daughter. He still writes poetry and has a wealth of knowledge on the music of the glam rock era.

Jeremy went into banking after leaving school and for the past ten years has been a business coach and trainer. He is married and takes great pride in his many nephews and nieces.

Robert did indeed study food technology and works as an account director for a global logistics business. He was married and has two daughters, but finds himself single at the moment. In his words, "watch this space!" He takes great pleasure in sailing.

Martin has a career with a large packaging company as an account manager. He too was married and has two children. He now lives with a new partner in Nottinghamshire. Martin always wanted to be a musician and, frankly, still has enough talent in that area to be one!

Andreas went into accountancy and emigrated to Australia where he lives with his wife and three children. He is currently a compliance and financial manager for an international company based in Sydney.

In 1981, Chris took his backpack to Sydney, Australia, where he now lives with his wife and three lovely children. He no longer owns hiking boots and still disputes Andrew Price's claim to having the tallest backpack on the Cleveland Way!

Andrew Price spent thirty years in Tasmania and has four children and a steadily increasing number of grandchildren living there. In 2014, he returned to the UK, back to the English countryside he loves and achieved a lifetime's ambition by writing these memories of walking the Cleveland Way.

I hope the book entertains and inspires. The North York Moors National Park ensures that the Cleveland Way will exist in beautiful surrounds for centuries to come. I thoroughly recommend you get some stout boots, wet-weather clothing and a map, and take to the hills yourself!

Acknowledgements

My parents, Mike and Mary, for their support and for being the initial inspiration to attempt the Cleveland Way.

Michael, Tristan and Carolyn Nichols, many thanks for running the farm in Tasmania in my absence.

My brother Douglas for all his help with the cover.

Joanne Marson, for her encouragement, for re-walking the Cleveland Way with me and for help with editing.

John Perkins for his original poetry *Why do you Love me Lord* and *On the Cliff of Sanity*, and for humorous memories from school.

Andrew Walbank for photographs.

All of the original walkers for their memories, contributions, laughter and friendship.

Terry and Sylvia Graveney for running the youth club in Long Clawson back in the early Seventies and for teaching us all the joys of walking, camping and map reading.

All the helpful people encountered while researching this book who live or work around the North York Moors National Park.

All those involved in maintaining the Cleveland Way walking track.

All those who care for their environment, especially those who don't drop litter when they are walking!

Request from the Holiday Fellowship inscribed on a rock by the side of the Cleveland Way east of the Lord Stones:

Friend when you stay or sit
And take your ease
On moor or Fell or under spreading trees
Pray leave no traces of your way side meal
No paper bag or scattered orange peel
Nor daily journal littered on the grass
Others may view these with distaste and pass
Let no one say and say it to your shame
That all was beauty here until you came.
(See, Chris, you shouldn't have dropped that orange
     peel!)

Playlist

Chapter 1
'Rave on' by Buddy Holly
'Oh Boy' by Buddy Holly
'Black Night' by Deep Purple
'Question' by The Moody Blues
'Still, you turn me on' by Emerson, Lake and Palmer
'I'll Be There' by The Jackson Five

Chapter 2
'Satisfaction' by The Rolling Stones
'Time in a bottle' by Jim Croce

Chapter 5
'Bony Moronie' by Larry Williams
'Back home' by the England Football Squad
'These Boots are made for walking' by Nancy Sinatra
'The Pushbike Song' by The Mixtures

Chapter 6
'Jealous mind' by Alvin Stardust

Chapter 7
'For those in peril on the sea'
'The road to Gundagai' – traditional Australian folk song
'American Pie' by Don McLean
'Streets of London' by Ralph McTell
'All you need is love' by The Beatles

Chapter 8
'The Happy Wanderer'

Chapter 9
'Street Fighting Man' by The Rolling Stones

Chapter 10
'Wandering Star' by Lee Marvin
'Daisy Bell'
'Roll out the Barrel'
'Down at the Old Bull and Bush'
'The Lambeth Walk'
'Ride a White Swan' by T Rex
'Dragons Ear' by T Rex
'I hear you knocking' by Dave Edmunds

Chapter 12
'Cum on feel the Noize' by Slade
'I'm gonna knock on your door' by Little Jimmy Osmond
'It's all over now' by The Rolling Stones

Chapter 13
'All things bright and beautiful'

Chapter 14
'Goodbye to love' by The Carpenters
'Ain't no sunshine' by Bill Withers
'Raining in my heart' by Buddy Holly
'Bye Bye Love' by The Everly Brothers
'Without you' by Harry Nilsson

Chapter 16
'When the Saints go Marching In'